D1645041

Oldbourne History of Science Library

THE
ENGLISH PARACELSIANS

To
Hans Schwenneke

THE
ENGLISH
PARACELSIANS

ALLEN G. DEBUS

Associate Professor of the History of Science
University of Chicago

OLDBOURNE
LONDON

OLDBOURNE BOOK CO. LTD
1-5 Portpool Lane, London, E.C.4

© *Oldbourne Book Co. Ltd, 1965*

UNIVERSITY
LIBRARY
NOTTINGHAM

540.942

N. . . . C.

WITHDRAWN JAN 1966

COUNTY LIBRARY

1101

Set in Bembo and Printed in Great Britain
by Jarrold and Sons Ltd, Norwich

Contents

List of Plates

Preface

SHORTLY before his death George Sarton wrote that "a history of Paracelsism is long overdue; it is badly needed for the understanding of medicine, chemistry, and philosophy not only in the Renaissance but also throughout the seventeenth and eighteenth centuries".[a] Commenting on Sten Lindroth's then recent study of Paracelsism in Sweden, he added that "such investigations should be carried through for the other countries of Europe and made available to the whole Republic of Letters".[b] The present work cannot claim to be a comprehensive history of Paracelsism, nor can it claim to be a complete discussion of all phases of English iatrochemical thought in the sixteenth and seventeenth centuries. Rather it is an attempt to define some of the major problems of concern to the English iatrochemists prior to 1640.

Chemistry prior to Robert Boyle and his late seventeenth-century colleagues has always presented a problem to historians of science. Occasionally the alchemists are lauded as the founders of modern chemistry, but more often they are dismissed as impostors whose occult speculations and dishonest dealings form no part of the history of science. Similarly, there is little agreement among modern commentators on Paracelsus. Some brand him a charlatan; others place him in the top rank of Renaissance natural philosophers. He has been described as a hero and as a villain of the Scientific Revolution. Until recently, however, few scholars have emphasized the fact that in Paracelsus and his

a George Sarton, *Appreciation of Ancient and Medieval Science During the Renaissance* (1st ed. 1955, Perpetua ed., New York, 1961), 5.
b *Ibid.*, 183.

followers there was a curious blend of the occult *and* the experimental approaches to nature. These men were neither exclusively "ancients" nor "moderns"—rather, their work reflects strongly both ancient philosophical thought and the opening phases of the Scientific Revolution. Along with their occult interpretation of the universe, the Paracelsians placed a new emphasis on chemistry as an aid to medicine, an emphasis which was to affect profoundly the development of both fields. On the theoretical as well as on the practical levels the work of these men is of major importance in the background of the late seventeenth-century chemists. And because the work of Boyle and his associates represents the culmination of late seventeenth-century chemistry, an investigation of the development of English Paracelsism has particular significance. The fact that Paracelsian thought developed somewhat differently in England than on the Continent adds to this interest.

Since the effective completion of the present manuscript a considerable number of important studies of Renaissance science have appeared which bear on topics presented here. Among them a few must be mentioned. W. P. D. Wightman's *Science and the Renaissance* (2 vols., Edinburgh and London, 1962) presents in a convincing manner the view of the author that the main contribution of Paracelsus was philosophical. Walter Pagel's recent monograph, *Das Medizinische Weltbild des Paracelsus: seine Zusammenhänge mit Neuplatonismus und Gnosis* (Wiesbaden, 1962) has reinforced his earlier contention that we may only approach an understanding of the Renaissance natural philosophers if we evaluate their total work (rather than fragments) in relation to the overall intellectual background of the period. Pagel asserts that

Die Absicht und Originalität des Paracelsus liegt in einer Synthese. Chemie und Medizin sind ihm nur Aspekte einer "kosmologischen Anthropologie" (p. 25).

Further light on the "occult" sources of modern science may be gleaned from the important study by Frances A. Yates—*Giordano Bruno and the Hermetic Tradition* (Chicago, 1964). On more specific topics the new *History of the Worshipful Society of Apothecaries of London, Volume I, 1617–1815* (by Cecil Wall, H. Charles Cameron and E. Ashworth Underwood—London, 1963) sheds new light on the relations of the Apothecaries and the Royal College of Physicians in the first half of the seventeenth century while Lloyd G. Stevenson's paper " 'New Diseases' in the Seventeenth Century" [*Bulletin of the History of Medicine, 39* (1965), 1–21] treats in authoritative manner a problem the Paracelsians exploited in their call for new medicines in a new age. Beyond the chronological limits of the present work Pyarali Rattansi's recent research has added appreciably to our knowledge of the Paracelsian-Helmontian revival of the mid-seventeenth century [see especially his "Paracelsus and the Puritan Revolution", *Ambix, 11* (1963), 24–32 and "The Helmontian-Galenist Controversy in Restoration England", *Ambix, 12* (1964), 1–23]. It should be noted further that the search for recent secondary sources is now greatly simplified with the publication of the *Paracelsus-Bibliographie 1932–1960 mit einem Verzeichnis neu Entdeckter Paracelsus-Handschriften (1900–1960)*, compiled by Karl-Heinz Weimann (Wiesbaden, 1963).

In the course of his research the author has become indebted to many individuals and organizations. He is grateful for the joint Fulbright and Social Science Research Council grant which made it possible for him to spend the year 1959–60 in England. The following year a Fels Fund award aided him in his research. More recently he has been the beneficiary of grants from the American Philosophical Society (Penrose Fund grant No. 2935), the National Science Foundation (Research grant No. G18548), and the National Institutes of Health (USPHS GM-09855) which have made it possible for him to complete certain aspects of his research which appear in the following pages.

He wishes also to thank the many librarians whose advice he has sought at the Widener and Houghton Libraries at Harvard, at the Boston Medical Library, and at the Cambridge University

Library, the British Museum, and the Wellcome Historical Medical Library in England. Dr. F. N. L. Poynter at the Wellcome Library, whose vast knowledge of Renaissance English medicine has simplified his research, deserves special recognition.

He is indebted, too, to many faculty members at Harvard and in England. He has imposed his problems—and sometimes his manuscript—on several people, among whom he particularly thanks Professor W. K. Jordan, Dr. E. I. Mendelsohn, Professor L. K. Nash, Dr. P. Rattansi, and Dr. George Basalla, who have been most helpful. He is grateful for the aid and suggestions of Professor Douglas McKie and Dr. W. A. Smeaton of University College, London; and he recalls a long and stimulating discussion with Professor J. R. Partington at Cambridge on the early history of the analysis of aqueous solutions. He also wishes to thank Mr. Desmond Geoghegan, editor of *Ambix*, for permission to include here the second chapter, much of the material for which first appeared in an article in that journal titled "The Paracelsian Compromise in Elizabethan England".[c] Mention must be made also of the warm interest and careful reading of the manuscript by Dr. Michael Hoskin, the editor of the series of monographs in which this volume appears.

His greatest debt is to Professor Walter Pagel in London and Professor I. B. Cohen at Harvard. Professor Pagel's lifelong study of Paracelsus and his followers has opened up an entirely new approach to Renaissance science, for which all scholars are in his debt. Beyond this, however, his personal interest in the author's research has helped clarify problems on innumerable occasions. Similarly Professor Cohen has responded to constant questions, and he has been of continual assistance in helping define the major problems that have arisen.

And finally he thanks his family: his parents for their continual aid and understanding, and his wife for her unparalleled patience and constant encouragement.

[c] *Ambix*, *8* (1960), 71–97.

Chapter One

Paracelsus and the Scientific Revolution

THE writing of the history of chemistry probably has a longer continuous tradition than that of any other science, yet it is the development of astronomy, physics and mathematics that recent histories of science have tended to emphasize in the period of the Scientific Revolution. These were the disciplines which represent the "progressive" elements of the intellectual ferment from which there developed the modern mathematical sciences. In contrast, the course of chemistry in the same period is often viewed with disdain because of its connection with alchemical trickery, astrological lore, kabbalistic analyses and occultism of all sorts—strains of thought, now alien to science, which the modern historian of science often lumps together under the damning category of "mysticism". Those who are most impressed by the mathematical aspect of modern physical science often find it difficult to comprehend the different climate of opinion which characterizes chemical studies in the sixteenth and seventeenth centuries. A good reflection of this general attitude may be seen in the work of Herbert Butterfield, who cites the twentieth-century commentators on alchemy as "fabulous creatures" who "seem under the wrath of God themselves; for like those who write on the Bacon-Shakespeare controversy or on Spanish politics . . . [they] seem to become tinctured with the kind of lunacy they set out to describe".[1] If we turn to some of the standard histories of medicine or chemistry we may likely find ourselves further confused. Historians of medicine have a tendency to imply that the work of Paracelsus belongs primarily to the history of chemistry,[2] while historians of chemistry at times suggest that the innovations of Paracelsus most properly should be considered as part of the history of medicine.[3]

If the work of Paracelsus and other major chemists of the sixteenth and early seventeenth centuries is characterized either as unworthy of discussion or as acting as a force which retarded the general growth of science, a true understanding of the period is made difficult if not impossible. There is a vast body of Renaissance chemical literature, and a large proportion of it was written not by gold-seeking alchemists, but rather, by scholars who honestly felt that the true key to nature's secrets was to be found in the study of chemistry. Today we can say that many of their explanations were incorrect, but to their contemporaries their work often seemed a stimulating force, moving man ever closer to a true understanding of nature.

Paracelsus

These "chemical philosophers" were inspired by various currents of thought—by a reaction against the ancient authorities and a belief that fresh observations of nature should form the basis of a new science; by a reliance on Hermetic, neo-Platonic and neo-Pythagorean philosophy; and above all, by a special interest in the application of chemistry or alchemy as the key not only to medicine, but to the wider problems of the universe and theology as well. Their high priest was the famous Swiss-German physician and surgeon Philippus Aureolus Theophrastus Bombastus von Hohenheim (1493–1541)—the man who called himself Paracelsus. Before outlining the Paracelsians' chemical view of nature let us sketch in rapidly the life of this unusual man.

Born at Einsiedeln, a small country town near Zürich, Paracelsus picked up some knowledge of medicine from his father who was the local physician. His father's interest in transmutation made it possible for the boy to learn some alchemical lore as well.[4] Tradition has it that several bishops were involved in the training of the young Paracelsus, as well as the abbot Johannes Trithemius who was famous as one of the greatest of all alchemists. Whether or not this is so, in 1502 the father and son moved to Villach where the boy served as an apprentice in the Fugger mines. Here he learned at first hand the metallurgical processes of the period, and he also observed the characteristics of diseases associated with men who worked in the mines. Later he was to write the first book ever composed on occupational diseases—his famous tract on the diseases common to miners.

At fourteen Paracelsus became a wandering journeyman scholar and he seems to have visited many Continental universities. It is possible that he stayed long enough at Ferrara to obtain an M.D. degree, but there is no real proof of this.[5] After 1510 there is fleeting evidence that he appeared from time to time in many areas of Europe and the Middle East—in his writings he refers to Holland, Scandinavia, Prussia, Tartary, the countries under Venetian influence—and he states that he was on the last boat out of Rhodes before that island fell to the Turks. On these journeys he worked as an army surgeon—a lowly post for anyone who had an M.D. degree since surgeons were equated with barbers at the time. Still, it was a post which would have made it easy for him to continue his travels on a continent then ravaged by constant wars and revolts.[6]

While in his thirties he tried to settle down—but he was a thoroughly impossible person who always managed to offend the people who were trying to help him. As a result he generally either left a town of his own accord soon after his arrival, or else was almost chased out by the solid citizens he offended. One gains some insight into the spirit of this man in his oft-quoted contemptuous address to the physicians of his day:

I am Theophrastus, and greater than those to whom you liken me; I am Theophrastus, and in addition I am *monarcha medicorum* and I can prove to you what you cannot prove. I will let Luther defend his cause and I will defend my cause, and I will defeat those of my colleagues who turn against me; and this I shall do with the help of the *arcana*. . . . It was not the constellations that made me a physician; God made me. . . . I need not don a coat of mail or a buckler against you, for you are not learned or experienced enough to refute even one word of mine. I wish I could protect my bald head against the flies as effectively as I can defend my monarchy. . . . I will not defend my monarchy with empty talk, but with *arcana*. And I do not take my medicines from the apothecaries; their shops are but foul sculleries, from which comes nothing but foul broths. As for you, you defend your kingdom with belly-crawling and flattery. How long do you think this will last? . . . Let me tell you this: every little hair on my neck knows more than you and all your scribes, and my shoe-buckles are more learned than your Galen and Avicenna, and my beard has more experience than all your high colleges.[7]

In 1527 Paracelsus had a real stroke of luck. The famous printer of Basel, Frobenius, became ill with a leg ailment which the local physicians could not cure. Hearing that Paracelsus was then in Strasbourg, Frobenius sent for him—and Paracelsus proceeded to cure him. While administering to his famous patient, Paracelsus was put in contact with a cultured group of Swiss humanists, men such as Oecolampadius and Erasmus. He became the personal physician to Erasmus, and Oecolampadius was influential in having him appointed city physician and professor of medicine. This was a city appointment, but it gave Paracelsus the right to lecture at the University.

True to form, Paracelsus treated the authorities with little tact. The medical faculties of most universities at this time were very conservative and put strong emphasis on ancient and medieval authorities such as Hippocrates, Galen and Avicenna. Paracelsus announced that he would have nothing to do with these revered authors and that he would lecture instead on the basis of his own experience. When he proceeded to do this, he did it not in Latin, the proper language of scholars, but rather in his own common Swiss-German dialect. To top it all off, at the traditional bonfire on St. John's Day he cast the *Canon* of Avicenna in the flames. Needless to say, the faculty hated him—and the students did as well. They called him Cacophrastus and wrote an insulting poem about him which purported to have been written by Galen and sent from Hell. The final blow came when Frobenius, his patron, died in October, 1527. Soon after this he became involved in a lawsuit with a church dignitary who refused to pay his fee. With everyone against him, Paracelsus' position became untenable and he had to leave town in haste without even his manuscripts.

For the remainder of his life he was a wanderer, appearing now at one town and now at another, never staying long at any one place. Yet this is the period when some of his most important works were written. At Nuremberg he wrote his treatise on syphilis—then a relatively new disease which seemed to be having almost as disastrous an effect on the population of Western Europe as the measles was having on the natives of the Caribbean. In this work Paracelsus attacked the most common current methods of treatment, guaiac wood and liquid mercury. Instead, he suggested that the physician should use a milder form of mercury which had been chemically altered—and that this should only be administered with carefully prescribed dosage. Although he managed to get through the press a few short tracts stating his views, Paracelsus was prohibited from publishing his *Eight Books on the French Disease* by a decree based on the opinion of the Leipzig Medical Faculty. In reality it is likely that the Fuggers were influential in this decision, because at this time they held the guaiac wood monopoly and were bound to suffer financially if the views of Paracelsus were accepted.[8]

At Beratzhausen he wrote his famous *Paragranum*, where he spoke of the bases of medicine as philosophy, astronomy,

alchemy and ethics,[9] and other works were written in rapid
succession in different cities. The modern edition of his scientific
and philosophical writings comes to fourteen volumes and there
are manuscripts which have yet to appear in print. He continued
his travels—writing constantly—until finally called to Salzburg
at the request of the bishop suffragan Ernest of Wittelsbach.
There he died in September, 1541, at the early age of forty-eight.

Mysticism, Magic, and Observational Science

At first glance the Paracelsian approach to nature seems far
from conducive to the growth of modern science. The works of
Paracelsus and his followers are riddled with a mysticism and
hermeticism that smacks more of the occult than of what we
would call science. Yet, archaic as this must seem to the
twentieth-century observer, this mystical neo-Platonic universe
was in the time of Paracelsus enjoying a new popularity due to
the attention focused on it by the Florentine Platonists of the
late fifteenth century.

In the reaction against Aristotelian scholarship, Platonic and
Pythagorean writings gained a new influence in many fields of
learning, and scientific subjects were no exception. In this
regard, neo-Platonic influences are often cited as one reason why
Copernicus was attracted to the idea of a heliocentric universe,
and certainly the new fascination with mathematics derives in
part from the Renaissance Platonic-Pythagorean inspiration.
Yet this very inspiration was at best a double-edged sword in
regard to science. On the one hand we might point to
Copernicus' search for mathematical simplicity in his re-
organization of the heavens,[10] Kepler's search for a new
mathematical expression of the motions of the planets, or even
Galileo's mathematical description of falling bodies, as positive
instances of the new mathematical approach to nature. Yet, on
the other hand, Kepler also saw a mathematical simplicity in his
attempt to fit the orbits of the planets within the regular solids,
while Galileo and almost everyone else was loath to discard the

divine circularity of nature. Today we would call the one attitude scientific and the other not. In the sixteenth and early seventeenth centuries such a distinction could not be as clearly drawn, and we find Paracelsians and mystical alchemists such as Robert Fludd, who felt that mathematics was indeed a requisite in any study of cosmology, but that it should be used to show the divine harmonies of nature in the relationships and correspondences of mathematical figures to the microcosm and the macrocosm. The quantification of the motion of a falling object would have been for Robert Fludd little more than a waste of time, when one could use this same tool to study the grander designs of the universe. Such a view of mathematics fits in well with passages in the *Timaeus*, rather than with the modern scientist's mathematical analysis of experimental results.

In the same way that it is difficult to separate the "modern" from the "archaic" in the mathematical thought of the Renaissance, it is also difficult to judge other concepts then current. One of the most widely held beliefs at the time was a conviction in the overall unity of nature and the macrocosm-microcosm concept. It was held that all things which exist are connected or have some relation to one another. Everywhere there might be found correspondences between the celestial and sublunary worlds, and man as the microcosm mirrors all aspects of the great world about him. At first glance one would hardly choose such a concept as positive and leading to a new science, yet even the macrocosm-microcosm universe can be shown to have been a stimulus toward a fresh appraisal of nature.

Paracelsian physicians—leaning on this macrocosm-microcosm analogy, and eager to reap the benefits for mankind—felt that man could and should seek out in the plant and mineral kingdoms those objects which correspond with the proper celestial bodies. Ridiculous? Yes, by our standards, but not if one accepts as they did the widely held belief that sublunary objects are often impressed by "signatures" which make them identifiable.[11] And regardless of the truth or fallacy of their basic beliefs, Renaissance scholars were thus being strongly urged to make a fresh investigation of nature. This conviction was echoed time and time again by the Paracelsians. Listen to Peter Severinus—a major Paracelsian theorist and the influential physician to the King of Denmark—exhorting his readers in 1571 to

sell your lands, your houses, your clothes and your jewelry; burn up your books. On the other hand, buy yourselves stout shoes, travel to the mountains, search the valleys, the deserts, the shores of the sea, and the deepest depressions of the earth; note with care the distinctions between animals, the differences of plants, the various kinds of minerals, the properties and mode of origin of everything that exists. Be not ashamed to study diligently the astronomy and terrestrial philosophy of the peasantry. Lastly, purchase coal, build furnaces, watch and operate with the fire without wearying. In this way and no other, you will arrive at a knowledge of things and their properties.[12]

This plea for a new investigation of nature was closely associated with the natural magic of the Renaissance. Vital or magical forces were seen at work everywhere in the universe, and man, as part of the vast encompassing chain of life, was able to participate in the great world about him. The term "magic" thus came to mean an observational and experimental study of the unexplained or occult forces of nature.[13] In the *Philosophy to the Athenians* Paracelsus speaks of the Creation as a divine magic which he contrasts with the ordinary natural magic of man— meaning here man's experimental or observational approach to an understanding of his environment.[14] John Baptista Porta echoed this general view when he wrote "I think that Magick is nothing else but the survey of the whole course of Nature. For, whilst we consider the Heavens, the Stars, the Elements, how they are moved, and how they are changed, by this means we find out the hidden secrecies of living creatures, of plants, of metals, and of their generation and corruption; so that this whole Science seems merely to depend upon the view of Nature".[15]

By Porta's definition the whole idea of natural magic is closely connected with the relation of macrocosm and microcosm.

Natural magic as man's legitimate investigation of nature had nothing to do with the traditional black magic. Instead, this form of magic was to be allied, and closely allied, with religion. This was the same attitude expressed by Roger Bacon[16] some two and a half centuries prior to Paracelsus, and in all alchemical works it was also inherent that true faith and the successful investigation of nature could not be separated. Paracelsus stated that the basis of occult philosophy or magic should rest on the three pillars of prayer, faith, and imagination.[17] Conjurations and ceremonies other than those used by the Church were to be rejected, but on the other hand the efficacy of black magic was never denied.[18] In short, since natural magic is allied with religion, it cannot be witchcraft.[19] Rather, it is an essential branch of knowledge: the proper way for man to learn of the universe about him.

As for the works of Aristotle, they had been judged heretical on many counts, yet they were still being taught in many universities. Natural magic, on the other hand, seemed to offer another method to interpret nature by a philosophy whose very existence depended on sacred scripture. Paracelsus felt that it was inconceivable that any Christian should prefer the atheistic Aristotle to this pious magic. Aristotelian thought was based on logic, but logic is useless for the growth of knowledge since it explains its own statements only and never adds anything new. In reality knowledge may be acquired by divine grace alone; either by some direct mystical experience or by direct experimentation in nature. As Pagel has summarized the argument,

by means of unprejudiced experiment inspired by divine revelation, the adept may attain his end. Thus, knowledge is a divine favour, science and research divine service, the connecting link with divinity. Grace from above meets human aspiration for knowledge from below. Natural research is the search for God.[20]

Strongly influenced by this religious-magical background, Paracelsus thus approved of a new experimental investigation of nature. Nevertheless, his distrust of the traditional works of the ancients was so great that he suggested that

a Physitian ought not to rest only in that bare knowledge which their Schools teach, but to learn of old Women, Egyptians, and such-like persons; for they have greater experience in such things than all the Academians.[21]

Surely this appeal, although beneficial to the rise of experimental science, was fraught with danger for the future, since it encouraged quacks and empirics of the worst sort.

Alchemy and Nature

There is little question but that this mystical neo-Platonic universe played an important part in the rise of modern experimental science. The special appeal and emphasis on alchemy and alchemical analogies by the Paracelsians is also easy to understand. Alchemy had developed in late antiquity and the earliest strictly alchemical writings are already strongly loaded with Gnostic and neo-Platonic mysticism. The macrocosm-microcosm analogy, the hosts of intermediary angels, the significance of astrologic portents, and tales of personal mystical experiences all form part of this literature. Yet at the same time alchemy was generally unthinkable without the laboratory and man's own attempt to observe and carry out experiments on the metals—or any other matter which might be at hand. Alchemy was in a sense a special approach to the general neo-Platonic universe, and this is one reason why there was an increased interest in the alchemical writings with the revival of the neo-Platonic and Hermetic literature.

It is similarly easy to understand why this scheme of the universe should have had a special appeal to Paracelsus and a whole school of physicians who followed him. The macrocosm-microcosm relationship suggests that by the proper study of nature a method of cure for man's bodily ills might be found. Furthermore, the search for health was an avowed aim of the alchemists.

This had not always been so. The alchemy of late antiquity had been obsessed with the search for artificial gold while only in the alchemy of ancient China do we find the major goal of alchemy to be the search for immortality. As the "elixir of life" this essentially Chinese concept made its way into the alchemical speculations of the Islamic authors in the eighth and ninth centuries.[22] When these texts became translated into Latin in the twelfth and thirteenth centuries, the search for longevity immediately became one aim of the Western adepts. For Roger Bacon it was an established fact that the furtherance of medicine was one of the major uses of alchemy, both in the preparation of remedies and in the more basic search for the prolongation of life. In his *Opus Tertium* (1267) he spoke of the physicians who taught how medicines should be sublimed, distilled, resolved, and submitted to other alchemical procedures.[23] However, he bemoaned the fact that although "almost no one knows how to make metals, even fewer men know how to perform those works which are of value for the prolongation of life".[24] Arnold of Villanova (1235–1311) and John of Rupescissa (mid-fourteenth century) continued to stress the medical side of alchemy which enabled the operator to separate the pure essence from the crude and useless residue—usually by distillation techniques.[25] As the son of a physician, and as a person who had been trained in alchemical and metallurgical processes as a boy, Paracelsus naturally became a spokesman for, and a contributor to, this Renaissance chemical world view.

One cannot over-emphasize the fact that chemistry or alchemy meant far more to a Paracelsian than it does to us today. It was not limited to the art of transmuting base metals to gold any more than to the search for chemically prepared medicines. This is not to say that the iatrochemists believed that such transmutations could not occur, or that practical pharmacy was unimportant to them: as long as there was any life left in the old concept of a transformable primal matter there would be reason to believe in transmutations. Surely Boyle and even Newton maintained this belief. And since almost all Paracelsians professed some branch of medicine, any phase of this chemical philosophy that had medical value was sure to be emphasized by them. However, when Paracelsus wrote his *Paragranum* and explained that medicine rests on the four pillars of philosophy, astronomy, alchemy and ethics, he insisted that alchemy offers us nothing less than an "adequate explanation of the properties of all the four elements".[26] Alchemy, that is, has as its province the study of the whole cosmos. This is not surprising, since, according to ancient cosmological schemes, a study of the four elements does not mean chemistry as we know it but rather an investigation of the spheres of these elements and their place in the universe. The importance of the Paracelsian definition here is in uniting the alchemical with the cosmological meanings.

This Paracelsian concept of alchemy in the sense of our modern word "science" was maintained by his followers. The first English Paracelsian, R. Bostocke, explained in 1585 that true medicine is nothing other than "the searching out of the secretes of nature", and this is to be carried out by resort to "mathematicall and supernaturall precepts, the exercise whereof is Mechanicall, and to be accomplished with labor". Thus medicine is equated with our science, but Bostocke goes on to state that the real name for it is "Chymia, or Chemeia, or Alchimia, & mystica & by some of late Spagirica ars".[27] In the same vein, Michael Maier insisted that to learn of the world about us, the investigator must turn to medicine and chemistry since medicine "hath much in it of Divinity having the same subject with the Creation and Generation".[28]

The Divine Alchemy of the Creation

The study of the Creation as an introduction to the understanding of the universe had been common since the days of the early Church Fathers. For the Paracelsians, who contrasted their mystical religious approach to nature with that of men who relied on the heretical writings of Aristotle, it became common to do the same thing. Their contribution to the hexaemeral tradition was to interpret the Creation as essentially a divine chemical separation. So in the *Philosophy to the Athenians*—a title reminiscent of the Pauline epistles—the author, either Paracelsus or one of his followers, discusses the Creation of the world, and his interest centers primarily on the formation of the elements.

This work is of special interest since it was often reprinted and was frequently quoted by both English and Continental authors. All things are said to come from the traditional prime matter which is at the same time uncreated and "prepared by the Great Artificer Himself".[29] This prime matter is called by Paracelsus the *Mysterium Magnum*—the great generating substance from which all other more special mysteries proceed. It stands to more particular substances in the same way that cheese may be considered the mystery for worms or milk the mystery for cheese or butter.[30]

God made all things from the *Mysterium Magnum* much as a sculptor carves a block of stone. Creation then is a separation, and indeed, there is a similarity between this and chemical separations.

The principle . . . of all generation was Separation. . . . If vinegar be mixed with warm milk, there begins a separation of the heterogeneous matters in many ways. The truphat of the minerals brings each metal to its own nature. So it was in the Mystery. Like macerated tincture of Silver, so the Great Mystery, by penetrating, reduced every single thing to its own special essence. With wonderful skill it divided and separated everything, so that each substance was assigned to its due form.[31]

The Creation was brought about in several stages. The first of these was the separation of the four elements. In the second the firmament was separated from the fire; spirits and dreams were separated from the air; fish, salt, marine plants and the like were separated from the water; and wood, stone, animals and land plants were separated from earth. This process of separation then continued further with a separation of things from objects which had already been differentiated. Thus dung is separated from men and animals rather than directly from the earth. These separations continue until a fourth stage is reached in which there is a reduction to the original prime matter.

A Paracelsian then could speak in terms of a universal chemical philosophy because the Creation itself was for him a chemical process. This was a theme that was constantly re-echoed by the followers of Paracelsus. The leading French Paracelsist of the sixteenth century, Joseph Duchesne, explained that:

God as the great workemaister and Creator separated first of all Light from Darknesse, and this Aetheriall Heaven, which wee beholde, as an fifth Essence, or most pure Spirite, or most simple spirituall body. Then hee divided Waters, from Waters; that is to say, the more subtill, Aiery, and Mercuriall liquor, from the more Thick, Clammy, and Oyely, or Sulphurous liquor. After that he extracted and brought forth the Sulphur, that is to say, the more grosse Waters, from the drye part, which out of the separation standeth like salte, and as yet standeth by it selfe apart.[32]

Elements and Principles

It is clear, then, that of prime importance to this chemical philosophy of the universe is an understanding of the elements. Already two basic systems of element theory had been outlined. In the *Philosophy to the Athenians* Paracelsus spoke primarily of the ancient Aristotelian elements: earth, water, air and fire. But he was also the one who introduced to chemical theory the three principles, sulphur, mercury and salt, and it was with the aid of these that Duchesne explained the Creation. In fact both authors admitted that there is only one true element—the prime matter or the *Mysterium Magnum*. Both the four elements and the three principles must proceed from this original basic stuff of the universe.

In the ancient system each of the four elements was associated with two of the qualities, hot, cold, dry and moist. The fact that each element had one quality in common with another meant that by adding form to substance transmutation could easily occur—as when by adding heat to water (moist and cold) there is produced air (moist and hot). Paracelsus used the four elements, but he dropped the concept of a conjunction of qualities and considered each element to stand for a power in its greatest intensity. Fire is simply hot, not a combination of the qualities hot and dry. This singleness of quality makes the word element seem more applicable. Further, the elements were material substances for the ancients while for Paracelsus the ordinary air and water we perceive are but crude approximations of the true spiritual elements.[33] For him the elements are the mothers of objects as earth is the mother of men and those things which grow from the earth. It is thus that man has in himself the impression of all other earthly objects since they are all from the same "mother". Similarly, water is the matrix for metals, stones, and gems as well as being the main substance or flesh of plants.[34]

The system of the three principles was an extension of the older Islamic sulphur-mercury theory of the metals which had been extensively employed in alchemical literature since the eighth century.[35] Geber had already added a third principle, arsenic, to these two, and had considered the three to have both spiritual and material properties in the metals; but the Geber modification was not universally accepted. The contribution of Paracelsus was to add salt as the third principle and extend the theory so that it might be used for all things rather than the metals alone. As in the earlier sulphur-mercury theory, the Paracelsian principles are not to be considered as the visible materials we see and call by these names. Rather, they are spiritual substances whose properties are resembled most closely in nature by sulphur, mercury and salt. Sulphur is the cause of combustibility, structure and substance. Solidity and color are due to salt, while the vaporous quality is due to mercury.

These three components, the combustible, the vaporous and the solid may be demonstrated by burning a twig.[36] Here one finds vaporous fumes (mercury), flame (sulphur) and ashes (salt).

Although all objects are composed of these principles, this is still a far cry from modern elemental theory. According to Paracelsus the three principles are qualitatively different in different materials. "There are as many sulphurs, salts and mercuries as there are objects."[37] Therefore even though it is possible to demonstrate the existence of the vaporous, the combustible, and the ashy properties in many substances on heating, one cannot use this system as the basis of any modern sort of analytical procedure. Modern chemical analysis developed from metallurgical assays (dry) and from the analysis of medicinal spa waters (wet). Paracelsians were to contribute to the spa water investigations, but such analyses were generally divorced from Paracelsian speculations on the three principles.

Unfortunately Paracelsus was not consistent in his use of the different systems. In the *Archidoxis* the elements are discussed on two different levels—body and soul. Here he spoke of pre-destined elements or the quintessence as the soul: and he referred to the four Aristotelian elements as the body, much as material substances. On the other hand, in most of his other works he spoke of the four elements on the highest level in their cosmic sense, as imperceptible elements or matrices. But in these same works he speaks of the elements on a "bodily" level also and here they are represented as perceptible elementary bodies in terms of the four concentric spheres of earth, air, water and fire—and he adds that all specific objects are made out of the three chemical principles.[38] Confusing?—Of course. It was a puzzle to his sixteenth- and seventeenth-century followers as well as to us today. In the *Philosophia de generationibus et fructibus quatuor elementorum* he states that

The world is as God created it. In the beginning He made it into a body, which consists of four elements. He founded this primordial body on the trinity of mercury, sulphur and salt, and these are the three substances of which the complete body consists. For they form everything that lies in the four elements, they bear in them all the forces and faculties of perishable things.[39]

Here the principles are used in the sense of entities having the ability to give form to the elements. But his works so abound in differing passages that some felt he meant that the elements were composed of the principles and others insisted that the principles are composed of the elements.[40] Because of this indecision in the works of Paracelsus himself it is not surprising that later iatrochemists utilized the four elements and the three principles as they wished, dropping some and relating the rest as they saw fit. The value of the three principles was to be found primarily in the fact that it was a working concept. The Aristotelians talked and speculated about the four elements; but the iatrochemists saw the vaporous, the combustible and the residuous fractions every time they ran an organic distillation.

Paracelsian Chemistry and the Microcosm

The experimental implications of the neo-Platonic cosmology and its astrology existed prior to the time of Paracelsus. And it is true that the alchemical writings were of interest to the Renaissance neo-Platonists. Yet it was a major contribution of Paracelsus to unite these two traditions far more strongly than they had been in the past so that nature in a sense became a vast chemical laboratory. We have already pointed to his explanation of the Creation as a divine chemical separation, but with the Paracelsians almost all processes of interest were to be explained in this fashion. The formation of the earth's crust could seem-ingly be duplicated in chemical flasks, mountain streams were explained in terms of earthly distillations, thunder and lightning were no less than the explosion of an aerial sulphur and niter, duplicating gunpowder on a grand scale, and the rains were due to macrocosmic circulations that imitated the heating of water in the alchemical pelican.[41]

Human physiology took on a special new meaning with the Paracelsians. Man had a special position in the universe in neo-Platonic thought and since the great world operated on chemical principles, so too must man. If Paracelsus still held to the four elements, he did discard the equally time-honored humors.[42] Disease according to the ancients was due to an imbalance of the four humors—blood, phlegm, yellow bile and black bile. Such an imbalance caused a disturbance of the whole body and it was the purpose of the physician to restore the proper original balance. With this sort of explanation it was impossible to differentiate the disease according to either the organ or the cause of the morbid condition. Paracelsus taught rather that diseases were often due to external causes and that they were localized in particular organs. According to Pagel, "he was actually the first to teach that there are different diseases which can be classified and that each disease is a peculiar reality, an Ens".[43] And since Paracelsus pictured disease as a chemical reaction within the body we again see chemical influences of importance: different types of disease arise because of the different interactions of the three fundamental principles with the elements. As similar interactions in nature give rise to the medicinal plants and minerals, it is the physician's duty to imitate these interactions to produce from some natural plant or mineral a derived product which will give an action against the disease.[44]

Diseases, then, are entities in themselves which may be distinguished by specific changes and causes; and furthermore, they are local processes which may be defined in chemical terms.[45] But in contrast with the ancient concept of the upset of the humors, they are regarded as being due to the introduction of certain "seeds" of disease into the body.[46] The physiology of the body is ruled over by *archei* acting more or less like internal alchemists in the different organs. The most important of these is the *archeus* of the stomach which separates the pure from the impure parts of the food, distributes the valuable portions to those parts of the body where they are needed, and discards the poisons. If the *archei* fail to act properly, poisons can accumulate within the body instead of being eliminated and when this happens disease can result.[47] A good example may be seen in Paracelsus' theory of tartaric disease which included such afflictions as are associated with the building up of stony precipitates in the body (e.g. the calculus, tartar of the teeth, or the calcifying material built up in the lungs in a case of tuberculosis).[48]

As long as disease was ascribed to an imbalance of the humors, effective medical diagnosis hardly existed, since little attention was paid to local seats and aspects of disease. Examination of the patient was generally considered unnecessary and the most common form of diagnosis was "water-casting"—the study of the patient's urine which could be brought to a specialist in this "art". Since the urine was regarded as a filtered overflow of the blood this was thought to be a valid procedure, and in general the patient's condition was judged from the quantity, the observable differences in the different levels, and the color of the sample.[49]

Here again Paracelsus broke with tradition and suggested instead that the only possible way to obtain valuable information from the urine was to subject it to a chemical examination. Thus, with the help of distillation and coagulation it would be possible to bring out the true colors of the samples as well as to make quantitative measurements based on weight. This emphasis on chemical distillation was as useless a procedure as that of the ancient and medieval doctors, but it was typical of the Paracelsian interest in chemical processes and their relation to the human body.[50]

The relationship of the great world to man could also be explained by reference to chemical analogies. The motion of the blood was at times compared to the great macrocosmic circulations of the heavenly bodies and the rains, which could be duplicated in the chemical "pelican". Again, it was likened to a connected series of chemical distillations within the body. In fact some iatrochemists postulated a chemically inspired theory of the circulation of the blood prior to the work of Harvey, and Harvey himself compared the circulation of the blood with the circulation of the earthly waters in the formation of rain.[51]

For the Paracelsian a direct intervention in man's affairs by divinity was seen to take place through the rays of the stars and especially by the "breath of the Lord". In either case our earthly atmosphere represented a medium through which the heavenly influences passed. This is one reason why Paracelsians were continually interested in the atmosphere and its relationship to man.[52] Here too chemical influences are seen in the action on the human body of the aerial sulphurs and niters—the latter being associated with the breath of the Lord. "Mystical" speculations of this nature on the constitution of the atmosphere by some of the later Paracelsians led to their rejection of blood letting—their argument being that the vital nitrous part of the air was chemically abstracted from the gross part and joined to the blood. Any loss of this vital substance could only result in harm to the entire body.[53]

Paracelsus and the Introduction of Chemically Prepared Medicines

If the bodily functions reduce to chemical reactions it should be expected that chemically prepared medicines would cure diseases. The Paracelsians became famous—or perhaps infamous —for their promotion of such remedies, especially compounds prepared from metals and minerals.[54] In itself this was nothing new, since the application of alchemy to pharmacy represents one of the medieval contributions to science. John of Rupescissa in particular seems to have applied the concept of separating the pure from the impure to the extraction of "virtues" from plant material as well as metals and minerals. This tradition had continued through the later Middle Ages and was still strong during the lifetime of Paracelsus. The latter, however, became so completely identified with this type of cure that within a few decades of his death the mere approval of any metallic remedies was enough for a doctor to be stamped as a Paracelsian by his more conservative continental colleagues.

As yet little agreement has been reached among scholars as to the extent of the innovation of Paracelsus in the introduction of mineral remedies. The pharmaceutical literature of the sixteenth century and earlier has not yet been sufficiently well explored for anyone to make definite statements about who originated what.[55] Multhauf has recently called attention to the survival of the medieval-alchemical distillation approach to chemical remedies in the *Archidoxis* of Paracelsus.[56] John of Rupescissa and his followers had been chiefly interested in distillations to obtain the quintessence or lightest fraction of the chemicals which were being worked with; with an interest centered primarily on the distillate rather than the residue, often little was recovered beyond the original solvent while the more important products of the reaction would remain in the *caput mortuum* which was discarded. Multhauf would thus place the real change in chemical preparations with the later Paracelsians who were willing to discard the distillate and work up the inorganic salts remaining behind in the residue. More recently, Schneider, in his intensive study of the sixteenth- and seventeenth-century German pharmacopoeias, has reached a different conclusion.[57] While willing to agree that the impact of metallic and mineral remedies only begins to make itself felt in the late sixteenth and early seventeenth centuries, he has pointed out that certain inorganic compounds of key importance—antimony, mercury and iron salts—derive directly from authentic Paracelsian texts rather than the earlier alchemical tradition.[58] In truth the later iatrochemists acknowledged their debt to both Paracelsus and the medieval alchemists.

If the remedies of Paracelsus himself were not always original, his use of them was laudable, for Paracelsus and his followers called attention to the fact that they went to great pains to determine the correct dosage with their medicines.[59] Indeed, such a precaution was essential, since Paracelsus believed that poisons ranked among the most effective medicines available to physicians. Here again we see a break with tradition, for Galenic medicine affirmed that "contraries cure"—that is, a medicine with an excess of the "hot" quality would restore to balance a humoral system that was predominantly "cold". Germanic folk tradition suggested an opposed theory, that like cures like. Here it was assumed that the poison that caused the complaint would—in proper dosage—also cure it. With his distrust of the ancients, and his sympathy for folk medicine, Paracelsus accepted this principle as valid, and it became one of the most distinctive hallmarks of his followers.[60] It was the essential task of the chemist to find ways to remove the toxic qualities of these drugs so that they might safely be administered internally. Thus Paracelsus carefully described the process of preparing potassium arsenate from the fusion of arsenic with saltpeter and he advocated the use of mercury compounds rather than the metal itself.[61]

It is likely that Paracelsus did do a great deal of experimenting himself, but there is relatively little of importance which can be traced back to his own experimental work. This is due partly to the fact that Paracelsus gave relatively few detailed chemical directions, but it must again be emphasized that much of the early chemical literature has yet to be examined in detail. While Multhauf has pointed to the archaic nature of most Paracelsian chemical preparations, Schneider has unearthed important innovations in his inorganic remedies. Kopp and Walden have also called attention to his preparation of drugs with narcotic effects such as the ether-like products which he prepared from the reaction of alcohol on sulphuric acid.[62] It is interesting that he showed the sleep-inducing properties of these compounds on chickens. More important was his attempt to separate the Aristotelian elements from the metals which was to familiarise the chemical world with the idea that things can be arranged in chemically similar classes the members of which were susceptible of chemically similar processes; whereby we reach the two important notions of chemical classes, and chemical processes.[63]

From what is now known of the strictly chemical aspects of his work, one may conclude that for the most part Paracelsus reflects the work of his alchemical predecessors—but he made significant additions both in actual compounds and hypotheses. These changes were not always evident in his own lifetime, but they were eventually to affect profoundly the work of his followers.[64]

The Influence of Paracelsus

The extraordinary influence of Paracelsus is not always easy to see in the twentieth century. He built his system on a chemically modified neo-Platonic cosmology which was not in itself a radical break with tradition, and as we have seen, his purely chemical achievements reflect the work of the late medieval alchemists rather than represent a totally new foundation for the science. Yet, both chemistry and medicine did change as a result of his work. To a very appreciable extent this was due to the inflammatory nature of his writings and his stirring call for reform, which brought forth controversies among scholars in all fields for the next century and a half. It was only ten years after Luther nailed his ninety-five theses to the door of the Castle Church at Wittenberg that Paracelsus burned the Canon of Avicenna in the St. John's bonfire at Basel.[65] This "Luther of Medicine" was a blunt man, crude and opinionated, yet at the same time he was the most revolutionary in spirit of all the great leaders of the Scientific Revolution. His ability to stir up controversy is reflected in the unsettled nature of his own life. Still, the controversial nature of the man did not extend much beyond his immediate physical location during his lifetime. His Greater Surgery was published in 1536 and was quite successful. Yet other than this and a few minor works, it was not until after his death that his writings began to be published in quantity. This is partly due to the fact that most of his works were written in German, a language considered unscholarly at the time,[66] and partly to the fact that by the middle of the sixteenth century physicians were beginning to feel the loss of the extensive Arabic commentaries on the ancients, which had been dropped in the initial humanistic attempt to revert to the original Greek texts of the classical authors. The works of Paracelsus supplied a new body of medical writings which helped fill this gap.[67]

But above all, physicians turned to Paracelsus because of the reports of remarkable, almost miraculous, cures. In 1550, only nine years after his death, Cyriacus Jacobus wrote of this remarkable man who had been able to cure the three gravest diseases: gout, leprosy, and epilepsy.[68] Three years later one of his major texts was published for the first time, the *Labyrinthus medicorum errantium*. A typical story is that of Adam of Bodenstein (1528–77), who served as physician to Otto, Count Palatine. Originally a Galenist, he fell ill himself of a tertian fever which with complications lasted for well over a year (1556). Finally, in despair, he accepted a Paracelsian remedy from a fellow practitioner and was completely cured in a month.[69] Adam, who was the son of the church reformer Carlstadt, became one of the first of the Paracelsian propagandists and he devoted much of the rest of his life to the publication of hitherto unpublished writings of Paracelsus with lengthy commentaries and expositions. In the 1560s these works began to appear in ever-increasing frequency, and by 1585 the English Paracelsian Bostocke could cite as Continental Paracelsians no less than the following: Cyriacus Jacobus, Petrus Severinus (physician to the King of Denmark), Albertus Wimpeneus, Adam of Bodenstein, Gerard Dorn, Michael Toxites, John Huernius, Leonhard Thurneisser, Joseph Duchesne, John Chrisippus, Michael Neander, Theodore Zwinger, Theodore Birckmann, D. Rochefort and Jean Liebaud.[70] Even the old Galenist teacher of

Vesalius, Winter von Andernach, began to study chemistry at the age of seventy and became a Paracelsian.[71] At last the die-hard Galenists began to take note of this spreading medical heresy. No longer was it a case of a single "maniac" throwing the works of the ancients into the bonfire. Now most of the Continent, certainly all of Germany, was becoming infested with these disciples of Paracelsus.

Galenist Reaction—The Attack of Thomas Erastus (1572)

The first comprehensive refutation of the Paracelsians was that of the Swiss physician and theologian, Thomas Erastus. He had been commissioned by the Duke of Saxony for this purpose, and in 1572–73 the four parts of his *Disputationes de Medicina Nova Paracelsi* appeared in print. Erastus was willing to grant to Paracelsus some credit for his ability as a chemist[72] and for pointing out some errors in Galen,[73] but in general Erastus stood as the foremost sixteenth-century defender of medieval tradition. For him Paracelsus was a dangerous innovator who advocated lethal poisons for medicines.[74] His various metallic remedies, especially the poisonous mercury compounds, were noted with alarm. If this were not bad enough, Erastus especially warned his readers about Paracelsus' association with the Devil and his use of magic.[75] He found Paracelsus to be a charlatan who could not be trusted, especially since he continually contradicted himself and, as a consequence of his neglect of logic, wrote in a totally disorganized and incomprehensible manner.[76]

Erastus was utterly opposed to the philosophic system of Paracelsus. The neo-Platonic unification of the corporeal and the spiritual with their continuous transition and conversion was objectionable to him for theological reasons. He could not accept the opinion of Paracelsus that Creation could be likened to a chemical separation.[77] Furthermore, he castigated Paracelsus for his conception of the microcosm. If man's body contained the virtues and materials of all parts of the world, then why was it not possible for him to fly, to lay eggs, to live in the sea, and to be able to do all the things that all or any of the other creatures could do?[78] He accused him of Gnosticism, and among other things complained of his belief in miracles, the power of amulets, and the use of spoken words in incantations.[79] In medicine—and Erastus like Paracelsus was a physician—he was at odds with his compatriot over the humoral system. To Erastus this was one of the crowning glories of Galenic medicine, and to assume that diseases are separate entities which enter man from the outside was incomprehensible.[80]

But even if he believed that the theory of Paracelsus could not be defended, he felt that it was not so much this that was causing men to be drawn to this medical heresy, as the reports of the wonderful cures. Accordingly Erastus searched the archives to obtain proof of notable failures in the attempts of Paracelsus to treat patients, and he was especially gratified to see that all those treated with Paracelsian methods at Basel had died within a year even if they had shown an initial improvement.[81]

Erastus placed special emphasis on the three principles—a truly monstrous innovation which deserved to be refuted at length. He felt that since sulphur, salt, and mercury are corporeal objects, they cannot be considered as principles, but even if they were taken to be incorporeal, as Paracelsus assumed, then they could not be upheld as the origin of the four elements, as it is impossible for anything corporeal to be made from something which is incorporeal.[82] For Paracelsus, all things are composed of what they may be dissolved into, and he had affirmed that he had been able to convert everything into his three principles. But Erastus argued that things do not consist of those substances from which they are generated, nor are the products of generation such as worms necessarily the constituents of the decaying body from which they have developed.[83] Heat, the most universal decomposing agent of the alchemists, changes bodies into substances which are not constituents of the original bodies. In fact, the degree of decomposition of a body varies in direct proportion with the degree of heat applied.[84] Certainly sulphur, salt, and mercury are never found as the products of a decomposition performed with heat. (It is interesting that these were the most powerful arguments to be used by Robert Boyle against the principles in his *Sceptical Chymist* nearly a century later.) For his part, Erastus held firmly to the traditional elements, and stated that if the chemical art does not decompose samples to the three principles, it does decompose them to the four elements.[85] He then went on to ask how Paracelsus could have made these errors. It was his view that Paracelsus had made his fundamental mistake in his concept of "element". In his belief in the noncorporeality of an "element" he was led to conceive of it as similar in nature to the spirit or soul of a substance, a concept which Erastus vigorously denied.[86]

Actually Erastus had touched on a sore point when he attacked the work of Paracelsus in regard to the three principles. Paracelsus had not been at all lucid when he had spoken of the elements, the principles, and their interrelation. The problem was further complicated by the fact that he treated these fundamental stuffs differently in his chief chemical work, the *Archidoxis*, from in the rest of his writings. This misunderstanding, combined with the individualism characteristic of most of his followers, led eventually to the anarchy in the teaching of the elements which is so typical of the seventeenth century. By this time almost every author who wrote a work dealing with chemistry included a section which gave his own—often unique—views of the elements or principles.[87] In the seventeenth century a five-element-principle system was most common, but just what the five were varied from one author to the next. This state of indecision remained current in the science until the Chemical Revolution of the late eighteenth century.

Summary

At the time of his death in 1541 Paracelsus had had few if any real disciples, yet thirty years later one may speak of a "Paracelsian school of physicians". This was due in part to the apparent newness of the Paracelsian system—the explanation of the great world and man as well in terms of chemical analogies. However, more important for the success of the Paracelsian doctrines was the dramatic call for a new medicine based on fresh observations. Because most of the works of Paracelsus were first published after his death, by his mid-century followers with their own commentaries, it sometimes becomes difficult to separate the original texts from the later additions or even to certify works as genuine—and there is often little point in trying to do so since the influence of the commentaries coincided with that of the master. Credence had been given to the writings of Paracelsus primarily because of the remarkable cures supposedly worked by him, reports which even his enemies often did not deny.

The Galenists, still entrenched in the medical schools, did their part to help publicize the Paracelsian theories. The work of Erastus was one of the first of the anti-Paracelsian blasts, but it was far from the last. The particularly bitter fight at Paris over the use of metallic remedies, at the beginning of the seventeenth century, is another case where the Galenists unwittingly publicized the views of the iatrochemists. By that period the name Paracelsus was familiar to almost everyone whether or not he was a physician. Even John Donne, comparing the work of Copernicus and Paracelsus, thought that Paracelsus deserved the title "innovator" more than the astronomer.

To a limited extent John Donne's appraisal was correct. Surely there is no question that the writings of the Paracelsians did give real stimulus to a new approach to nature. In the sixteenth century there was no group calling more loudly for a revolt against man's over-reliance on the writings of the ancients. All Paracelsians insisted that the study of medicine and nature should be based on fresh observations and experiments rather than the outdated writings of an Aristotle or a Galen—and they called for a revision of the university curricula on this basis.

Also basic to Paracelsian thought was the conviction that chemistry or alchemy should serve as the key to the secrets of the universe. Here again we might well feel sympathetic to their viewpoint. Alchemy as it existed *c.* 1550 had associated with it an experimental side—perhaps proto-experimental would be a better term—while physics and the study of motion still remained for the most part in the hands of the commentators on Aristotle. Yet chemistry was not for the Paracelsians what it is for us. For them it was an aid to man on two levels. *First,* chemistry formed the basis for an understanding of the macrocosm as a whole. They felt that the universe was chemically created and that it continues to operate in a chemical fashion. They asserted that if we study nature through chemistry we will learn not only of the created universe, but of our Creator as well. The religious overtones connected with the Paracelsian philosophers were not unimportant in a period which was witnessing the Reformation struggle between Protestants and Catholics. *Second,* the Paracelsians turned their chemical key towards an understanding of the human body—an approach they believed valid since they maintained that our bodies, which are in close correspondence with the macrocosm, must also operate chemically. Bodily functions were chemical functions and diseases were pictured as chemical malfunctions which chemically prepared medicines would counteract and cure.

The chemical philosophy of the Renaissance Paracelsians is therefore important for the rise of modern science especially for two reasons: for its attack on ancient tradition and authority, and for its search for physical truth through chemistry—this being associated with the redirection of the aims of the chemist toward medicine and an understanding of the universe. Yet one does not have to dig deeply to see that these progressive aspects are only part of the picture. Much of their philosophy we would today call non-scientific or even anti-scientific. In their search for a philosophical basis for their thought they accepted the Pythagorean, neo-Platonic and Hermetic approach which already formed part of their alchemical heritage. This did not seem a reactionary step to them as it may to us—largely because the neo-Platonic writings were considered to be an acceptable alternative to the work of Aristotle in the Renaissance. The success of the neo-Platonic-Pythagorean revival was affecting many fields other than chemistry. But while neo-Platonism had a certain newness associated with it, and while it formed part of the chemical writings the Paracelsians read and re-read with care, at the same time it had the unfortunate effect of stamping mysticism as well as experimentalism on these men. As a result, the Paracelsians represent a strange half-way house on the road to modern science. On the one hand man by his own effort may search for the secrets of nature. On the other hand man begins his search with preconceived notions of the macrocosm and the microcosm and the divine alchemy of the Creation—notions embellished with the dreams and fantasies of the late neo-Pythagorean and neo-Platonic authors. Renaissance man was stimulated by this heady mixture of occultism and science and the contradiction we see today did not seem to many sixteenth-century scholars to exist.

Notes for Chapter One

1. Herbert Butterfield, *The Origins of Modern Science 1300–1800* (New York, 1952), 98.

2. Major exceptions to this generality are the recent Paracelsian studies by Walter Pagel, chief of which is his authoritative *Paracelsus* (Basel, 1958). This and other more specialized papers by him will be frequently referred to in the course of this chapter. An excellent recent summary of the philosophical background to the work of Paracelsus and his contribution to the theory of disease will be found in Lester King's *The Growth of Medical Thought* (Chicago, 1963), 86–138. Representing the more traditional viewpoint, Charles Singer wrote his *Short History of Medicine* (New York, 1928) without referring to Paracelsus once.

3. Note the contradictory statements that may be found in the following works: E. J. Holmyard, *Makers of Chemistry* (Oxford, 1946), 115; Charles Singer, *A Short History of Scientific Ideas to 1900* (Oxford, 1959), 200; J. R. Partington, *Short History of Chemistry* (2nd ed., London, 1951), 42. When one turns from

these elementary accounts to more detailed studies one often finds long lists of chemicals known to or described by Paracelsus, but little appreciation or sympathy for his "mystical" speculations—a term usually applied in its worst modern sense. This traditional approach is maintained by Marie Boas[Hall] in her *Robert Boyle & Seventeenth-Century Chemistry* (Cambridge, 1958).

4. Pagel, *Paracelsus*, 8. I have relied primarily on this most recent account (pp. 5–29) for this short biography. Other references will be found in the bibliography.

5. *Ibid.*, 10. Evidence in support of Paracelsus' statement that he had been made a *Doctor utriusque medicinae* at Ferrara is discussed by W. Pagel and P. Rattansi in "Vesalius and Paracelsus", *Medical History, 8* (1964), p. 317. Here the acceptance of Paracelsus' affirmation to this effect by a magistrate at Basel and the address to Paracelsus as *beider arznei doctori* in the introductory letter to the *Grosse wundarznei* by Dr. Wolfgang Thalhauser, municipal physician at Augsburg, are cited as being of special importance.

6. Pagel, *Paracelsus*, 13–14. For a detailed but somewhat fanciful account of the journeys of Paracelsus, see Basilio de Telepnef, *Paracelsus: A Genius amidst a troubled World* (St. Gall, 1945), *passim*.

7. This famous passage has been translated often. Rather than offer a new version I have reproduced the translation given in Paracelsus, *Selected Writings*, ed. with an introduction by Jolande Jacobi, trans. Norbert Guterman (New York, 1951), 79f. For the original text see Paracelsus, *Sämtliche Werke*, ed. Karl Sudhoff and Wilhelm Matthiessen (15 vols., Munich and Berlin, 1922–33), *8*, 63–65; from the *Paragranum*.

8. Pagel, *Paracelsus*, 24.

9. *Ibid.*, 24–25.

10. On neo-Platonism and the sun-centered universe see Allen G. Debus, "The Sun in the Universe of Robert Fludd", *Actes* of the Colloque international organisé par l'Institut pour l'Étude de la Renaissance et de l'Humanisme de l'Université de Bruxelles: "Le Soleil à la Renaissance—Sciences et Mythes" (in press).

11. Pagel, *Paracelsus*, 221f. Hence, if a man needed to concentrate solar forces on his body, he should seek out what is solar among plants and minerals and apply them when the sun prevails in the aspect of heaven. On the doctrine of signatures see Paracelsus in the *Liber de Imaginibus*, in *Sämtliche Werke, 13*, 376–78. A major difference between neo-Platonic and Platonic thought is that although the lofty intellectual design of Plato was retained by neo-Platonists, Plotinus felt obliged to borrow from the Stoics since they had worked out a series of intelligences to explain the emanation from the deity down to the intellect of man.

12. Petrus Severinus, *Idea Medicinae Philosophicae* (3rd ed., Hagae Comitis, 1660), 39.

13. Pagel, *Paracelsus*, 223. Alex. Koyré, *Mystiques, spirituels, alchimistes: Schwenck-feld, Seb. Franck, Weigel, Paracelse* (Paris, 1955), 50, note 2. Giorgio de Santillana, *The Age of Adventure: The Renaissance Philosophers* (New York, 1956), 14. The Pagel citation is of particular interest for the relationship of magic to medicine.

14. Paracelsus, *Opera*, ed. J. Huser (2 vols., Strassburg, 1616), *2*, 3.

15. John Baptista Porta, *Natural Magick* (New York, 1957), 2.

16. Roger Bacon, "Epistola Fratris Rogerii Baconis de Secretis Operibus Artis et Naturae, et de Nullitate Magiae", Fr. Rogeri Bacon, *Opera Quaedam Hactenus inedita*, ed. J. S. Brewer (London, 1859), 526–32.

17. Paracelsus, *Of the Supreme Mysteries of Nature*, trans. R. Turner (London, 1655), 29–31. This work includes "Of the Secrets of Alchymy: Discovered, in the Nature of the Planets", 1–28; "Of Occult Philosophy", 29–90; and "Of the Mysteries of the Signes of the Zodiack", 91–158. Although probably written by Gerard Dorn, the English translation was ascribed to Paracelsus, and the *De Occulta Philosophia* was included in the Huser *Opera*. On the authenticity of this work see Paracelsus, *Sämtliche Werke*, *14*, 516.

18. Paracelsus, *Of the Supreme Mysteries of Nature*, 39. *Sämtliche Werke*, *14*, 516.

19. Paracelsus, *Of the Supreme Mysteries of Nature*, 81–82. *Sämtliche Werke*, *14*, 538.

20. Walter Pagel, "Religious Motives in the Medical Biology of the XVIIth Century", *Bull. Inst. Hist. Med.*, *3* (1935), 98f.

21. Paracelsus, *Of the Supreme Mysteries of Nature*, 88. *Sämtliche Werke*, *14*, 541.

22. F. Sherwood Taylor, *The Alchemists, Founders of Modern Chemistry* (New York, 1949), 68–75; John Read, *Prelude to Chemistry* (New York, 1937), 120ff.; Ho Ping Yü and Joseph Needham, "The Laboratory Equipment of the Early Medieval Chinese Alchemist", *Ambix*, *7* (1959), 57–117.

23. Roger Bacon, *op. cit.*, 40f. Bacon cited as authorities Avicenna and the spurious *Dinamidiarum* of Galen.

24. *Ibid.*, 41.

25. See Pagel, *Paracelsus*, 248–58; Robert P. Multhauf, "John of Rupescissa and the Origin of Medical Chemistry", *Isis*, *45* (1954), 359–67; "The Significance of Distillation in Renaissance Medical Chemistry", *Bull. Hist. Med.*, *30* (1956), 329–46; "Medical Chemistry and the Paracelsians", *Ibid.*, *28* (1954), 101–26.

26. Paracelsus, *Sämtliche Werke*, *8*, 55f.

27. R. B., Esquire (R. Bostocke), *The difference betwene the auncient Phisicke, first taught by the godly forefathers, consisting in vnitie peace and concord: and the latter Phisicke proceeding from Idolaters, Ethnickes, and Heathen: as Gallen, and such other consisting in dualitie, discorde, and contraretie. And wherein the naturall Philosophie of Aristotle, doth differ from the trueth of Gods worde, and is iniurious to Christianitie and sounde doctrine* (London, 1585), Sig. Bi (r).

28. Michael Maier, *Themis Aurea. The Laws of the Fraternity of the Rosie Crosse* (London, 1656), 27.

29. Paracelsus, "Philosophia ad Athenienses", in *Opera*, *2*, 2.

30. *Ibid.*

31. *Ibid.*, 3.

32. Joseph Quercetanus (Joseph Duchesne), *The Practise of Chymicall, and Hermeticall Physicke*, trans. Thomas Tymme, Minister (London, 1605), Sig. Hi.

33. Pagel, *Paracelsus*, 93ff.

34. *Ibid.*, 96–98.

35. The derivation of the sulphur-mercury theory is still open to some question. Generally it is described as an extension of the Aristotelian smoky and watery vapors in the process of turning into stones and minerals on the one hand and metals on the other. The Islamic authors, according to this explanation, postulated that the two exhalations actually undergo an intermediate conversion. The dry and smoky exhalation is changed to sulphur, and the watery exhalation is converted to mercury. Through a combination of the sulphur and the mercury, metals are formed. If they are pure and unite in the correct proportions, the result is gold. This interpretation of the evolution of the sulphur-mercury theory has been challenged by R. Hooykaas, who suggests that the theory is actually due to a Stoic interpretation of Aristotelian thought. He argues that the Aristotelian *hyle* or base matter is not a substance with an existence of its own, but rather it is "the sheer potentiality of being". Stoic philosophers changed this *hyle* into a material substance which could be differentiated into specific substances by means of the all-pervading, quality-bestowing *pneuma*. A dichotomy already present in Aristotle between the active and passive elements was also adopted and extended by these Stoics until in early alchemical thought there were two strands represented. The first, deriving directly from Stoic thought, was concerned with the dichotomy of active and passive "spirits"—that is, the contrast between volatile, color-giving substances such as sulphur, arsenic and mercury, and passive substances such as the chemical tetrasomy, the mixture of the base metals. There was also a purely chemical dichotomy developed by the Islamic authors in which the active principle was considered to be mercury. This was in use as the sulphur-mercury theory of the metals, but both of these systems of thought found expression in medieval Western writers, and those writers who seek to find a chemical trichotomy in the literature prior to Paracelsus are mistaken, for triads of sulphur, mercury and arsenic mentioned by Geber, Albertus Magnus and others are used really in the sense of the active spirits rather than as principles—that is, in terms of the first, rather than the second, dichotomy. See R. Hooykaas, "Die Elementenlehre des Paracelsus", *Janus*, *39* (1935), 175-88; "Chemical Trichotomy before Paracelsus?", *Arch. int. d'hist. des sci.*, *28* (1949), 1063-74. Pagel in *Paracelsus* (270 ff.) opposes this view and shows that sulphur, arsenic and mercury have both corporeal and spiritual natures in the *Summa* of Geber.

36. *Sämtliche Werke*, *11*, 348: "dan alles was im feur reucht und verreucht ist mercurius, was brennet und verbrennet ist sulphur und alles was aschern ist, das ist auch ein sal." This is from Paracelsus' *Die 9 Bücher de Natura rerum*. A translation of this work may be found in *The Hermetic and Alchemical Writings of Paracelsus*, ed. A. E. Waite (2 vols., London, 1894), *1*, 150.

37. *Sämtliche Werke*, *3*, 42 f., from the *De mineralibus*. Note should also be made of the fact that an analogy was often drawn between the three members of the Holy Trinity and the three principles.

38. Hooykaas, "Elementenlehre des Paracelsus", 175-77.

39. *Sämtliche Werke*, *13*, 12 f., from the *Astronomia Magna*.

40. On Paracelsus' meaning of the principles see Pagel, *Paracelsus*, 100–4.
41. These are topics to be referred to in greater detail in Chapters 3 and 4. See also Debus, "The Paracelsian Aerial Niter", *Isis*, 55 (1964), 43–61, and Debus "Gabriel Plattes and his Chemical Theory of the Formation of the Earth's Crust", *Ambix*, 9 (1961), 162–65. Pagel has discussed this in regard to Fludd in his "Religious Motives", 280 ff.
42. Pagel, *Paracelsus*, 132 f.
43. Pagel, "Religious Motives", 104.
44. Pagel, *Paracelsus*, 133.
45. *Ibid.*, 157 f.
46. *Ibid.*, 137–40.
47. *Ibid.*, 104–10.
48. *Ibid.*, 153–61.
49. For a discussion of urinoscopy in Tudor England see W. S. C. Copeman, *Doctors and Disease in Tudor Times* (London, 1960), 118–22.
50. Pagel, *Paracelsus*, 189–99.
51. For the Paracelsians and the circulation see Chapter 3 and also Allen G. Debus, "Robert Fludd and the Circulation of the Blood", *J. Hist. Med.*, 16 (1961), 374–93.
52. See below, Chapter 3, and also Allen G. Debus, "The Paracelsian Aerial Niter" (cited above, note 41).
53. Allen G. Debus, "Paracelsian Doctrine in English Medicine", *Chemistry in the Service of Medicine*, ed. F. N. L. Poynter (London, 1963), 5–26, esp. 17.
54. See the work titled "Concerning the Book of Alchemy without which no one can become a Physician" extracted from the *Labyrinthus Medicorum* and translated in *The Hermetic and Alchemical Writings of Paracelsus*, 2, 165–68. Also see the second book of the *Grossen Wundarznei*, *Sämtliche Werke*, 10, 277.
55. Wolfgang Schneider, "A Bibliographical Review of the History of Pharmaceutical Chemistry (with particular reference to German literature)", *Amer. J. Pharmaceutical Educ.*, 23 (1959), 168.
56. Sudhoff considered the *Archidoxis* to be the chief work of Paracelsus dealing with medicinal chemistry and the "fundamental text of the new specific therapeutics on a chemical basis": "The Literary remains of Paracelsus", *Essays in the History of Medicine* (New York, 1926), 275. On the views of Multhauf see the papers already cited, especially "Medical Chemistry", 105 and the "Significance of Distillation", 337–44.
57. Wolfgang Schneider, *op. cit.*; and "Die deutschen Pharmakopöen des 16. Jahrhunderts und Paracelsus", *Pharmazeutische Zeitung*, 106 (1961), 3–15; and "Der Wandel des Arzneischatzes im 17. Jahrhundert und Paracelsus", *Sudhoffs Archiv*, 45 (1961), 201–15.
58. Schneider, "Der Wandel", 208–14.
59. *Sämtliche Werke*, 7, 300 f.; Pagel, *Paracelsus*, 275 f.; Henry M. Pachter, *Paracelsus, Magic Into Science* (New York, 1951), 128.
60. *Sämtliche Werke*, 8, 107. This reference, dealing with the life-like principle, is from the *Paragranum*.

51. Pagel, *Paracelsus*, 145 with reference to *Von d. naturl. Dingen*. See also J. R. Partington, *A History of Chemistry*, 2 (London, 1961), 146.

52. Hermann Kopp, *Geschichte der Chemie* 4 (Braunschweig, 1847), 300; P. Walden, "Paracelsus und seine Bedeutung für der Chemie", *Angewandte Chemie*, 1941 (b), *54*, 421–27; additional points are brought forth by Walter Pagel, *Das Medizinische Weltbild des Paracelsus seine zusammenhänge mit Neuplatonismus und Gnosis* (Wiesbaden, 1962), 22–23.

63. T. P. Sherlock, "The Chemical Work of Paracelsus", *Ambix, 3* (1948), 52. Multhauf has pointed to the fact that the "separation of the elements" occurs in non-Paracelsian texts. See his "Significance of Distillation", 338.

64. The most recent surveys of Paracelsus' chemistry may be found in J. R. Partington, *History of Chemistry*, *2*, 115–51 and Walter Pagel, *Medizinische Weltbild*, 17–32.

65. On the question of the burning of the *Canon* by Paracelsus, see Pagel, *Paracelsus*, 20 f., and Lynn Thorndike, *A History of Magic and Experimental Science* (8 vols., New York, 1923–58), 5, 438 f. Pagel cites Sebastian Franck's 1531 reference to the event.

66. Thorndike, *op. cit.*, 5, 620.

67. *Ibid.*

68. Partington, *History of Chemistry*, 2, 146.

69. The testimony of Adam of Bodenstein is translated by Pagel in his *Paracelsus*, 126.

70. Bostocke, *op. cit.*, sig. Jii (r) through Jiii (r).

71. Partington, *History of Chemistry*, 2, 121–22.

72. Thomas Erastus, *Disputationes de Medicina Nova Paracelsi. Pars Altera in qua Philosophiae Paracelsicae Principia et Elementa explorantur* (s.l., 1572), 3. "Arbitror etiam Chemiam ipsum non leviter solùm & perfunctoriè attigirse, sed prorsus studiosè coluisse. Si quid fuit in eo laudabile, unum hoc fermè videtur commendari posse, quòd pharmacorum quorundam praeparationes docuit."

73. See Pagel, *Paracelsus*, 328 f. for a reference to Erastus' approval of Paracelsus in pointing out an error of Galen in a case of epilepsy.

74. *Ibid.*, 313. Here Pagel cites the fourth part of Erastus' *Disputationes* which was not available to the present author for consultation.

75. Erastus, *op. cit.*, 2. At this point Erastus accuses Paracelsus of being a magician, and calling the Devil his friend.

76. Thomas Erastus, *Disputationes de Medicina Nova Paracelsi. Pars 1 in qua quae de remediis superstitiosis et magicis curationibus prodidit praecipue examinantur* (Basel, s.a. [1572]), 16. At this point Erastus speaks of the "monstrosae Paracelsi cõtradictiones".

77. *Ibid.*, 4. In referring to the account of Creation in the *Philosophy to the Athenians* and its doctrine that the Creation was a separation, Erastus objects that: "Nihil tam praeposterè, tam inconditè, tam monstrosè, tam imple, tam sacrilegè scriptum excogitari potest, quam sunt in hunc librum ex spurcissima mente expuit."

78. Pagel, *Paracelsus*, 323 f. This reference is from the third part of the *Disputationes*.
79. Pagel, *Paracelsus*, 315–18.
80. *Ibid.*, 324–26. From Parts 3 and 4 of the *Disputationes*.
81. *Ibid.*, 327. Cited by Pagel from Part 4 of the *Disputationes*.
82. Erastus, *Disputationes* . . . *Pars altera*, 37–39.
83. *Ibid.*, 42–43.
84. *Ibid.*, 72.
85. *Ibid.*, 73. "Ultimè in elementa resolvi cernimus omnia: in salem, sulphur, & mercurium, solvi nullus homo verax constanter defendet."
86. *Ibid.*, 44–48, gives a general discussion of this problem.
87. As an example, see H. Metzger's discussion of the systems of elements and principles as propounded by the French chemists Béguin, Davisson, de Clave, Arnauld, Lefèvre, Glaser, and de Tressel in *Les Doctrines chimiques en France du début du XVIIe a la fin du XVIIIe siècle. Première partie* (Paris, 1923), 36–93 *passim*.

Chapter Two

The Elizabethan Compromise

ALTHOUGH Paracelsian thought spread rapidly on the Continent after 1550, it went almost without mention in England until the mid-1570s. Because of this, Elizabethan physicians became acquainted with chemically prepared medicines through the recipe books of Hieronymus Brunschwig, Conrad Gesner and others who favored the medieval—and relatively non-controversial—alliance of alchemy and medicine. The theoretical aspects of Paracelsian thought were made available in detail only after most medical men had already had their first taste of this body of writings at second hand— through the defamatory works of Thomas Erastus. The outcome of the Paracelsian struggle in England was thus determined from the outset. Chemical medicines which proved useful in combating disease were to be accepted whether or not they were specifically called "Paracelsian"—the medical fraternity had been properly prepared for them. On the other hand, the Paracelsian mystical universe was introduced to learned circles by way of the major attack on it, and with very few exceptions this alchemical cosmology became the object of distrust and suspicion during the Elizabethan period.

In recent years, some studies bearing on the introduction of chemically prepared medicines in England have appeared from Georg Urdang and Paul H. Kocher.[1] These papers represent significant contributions to the history of the Paracelsians, and yet their findings leave some questions still unanswered. What, for instance, was the role of the Royal College of Physicians in the introduction of Paracelsism in England? Professor Kocher states that this organization was "tough-minded, clannish, and reactionary" and decidedly against the new remedies.[2] On the other hand, Professor Urdang has shown that one-third of the members of the Pharmacopoeia Committee established by the College in 1589 had graduated from those European universities which led in the promulgation of chemical therapy. None of them had graduated from Paris, which was the chief stronghold of the most conservative Galenists.[3] His study of the proposed pharmacopoeia of 1585 would certainly indicate that the most influential medical group in England was not opposed to "Paracelsian" remedies.

But what is meant by the broad term "Paracelsian"? Both Professors Urdang and Kocher are primarily interested in the introduction of chemical therapy, and since Paracelsus was considered the leader of this group in the sixteenth century, they apply the name to the proponents of chemical medicines.[4] This surely is an admissible use of the word, but in the sixteenth century most of these men would have called themselves "chemists" or "chemical physicians" to distinguish themselves from those charlatans and empirics who were making free use of the term. Furthermore, it is necessary to keep in mind that Paracelsian remedies were but a small part of the Paracelsian system. There was as much, if not more, disagreement over the comprehensive theories of Paracelsus as there was over his practical reforms. The theoretical "Paracelsians" often disowned the work of the Swiss alchemist-physician because of their belief in their own originality—even though we may see Paracelsian thought reflected in their writings. One may conclude that the term had a very broad and loose meaning in the sixteenth and seventeenth centuries and was certainly not confined to chemical pharmacy. We are led to the further conclusion that it is necessary to discuss the work of the Paracelsians on several levels. Those interested in the theoretical work of Paracelsus often paid little attention to his practical medical reforms. Those interested in the latter, on the other hand, were not simply limited to men who wished to utilize chemically prepared medicines, since there was at the same time a tendency to apply chemical methods and analogies to a broad spectrum of problems.

The Medical Background in England

If the physicians on the Continent were already in dispute over the relative merits of the old and new medicines shortly after the middle of the century, the English were as yet untouched by this medical heresy. The first half of the sixteenth century was a period of medical humanism and the English were in the forefront of this "research". Medical truth was to be found not so much in observation as in the resurrection of the purified texts of the ancients. Thomas Linacre (1460–1524), chief among the founders of the Royal College of Physicians (1518), had obtained his M.D. degree at Padua (*c.* 1492), and there he had diligently sought previously unknown Greek texts of the ancient medical authorities. These he published with his own translations. Linacre, with many of his colleagues who were founders of the College, excelled in this typically Renaissance form of scholarship. In 1541, half a century after Linacre graduated at Padua, the equally famous John Caius (1510–73) obtained his degree there. The times were rapidly changing, but the emphasis of English medical scholarship remained the same as in the days of Linacre. The prominent physician and author Andrew Boorde (1490–1549) observed that "It is vaine curiositie when wee pry into the secretes of God, which belonge not to us",[5] and as late as 1559 when Dr. John Geynes suggested that Galen was not infallible, he was forced to sign a recantation before being received back into the company of the Royal College.[6]

The year of Caius' graduation was also the year of the death of Paracelsus. Caius was an intimate friend of Conrad Gesner, a man aware of most current trends in all fields of scholarship—and an influential proponent of chemically prepared medicines. In Padua Caius had lived in the house of Vesalius, and on his way back to England he had stopped at Basel where he must have heard of the teachings of Paracelsus. Yet, while we may cite his work on British dogs and his description of the sweating sickness as examples of observational science, nowhere in his writings is there to be found an acquaintance with Vesalian anatomy or Paracelsian theory.[7] Instead we find a continued emphasis on typical humanistic studies—commentaries on Galen and Hippocrates and a work on Greek pronunciation.

Although the works of Paracelsus and his disciples did not yet issue from the English presses, tomes on chemical remedies and methods were available from the English book dealers.[8] Hieronymus Brunschwig's book on distillation was "Englished" by Lawrence Andrew in 1527, and while it combined the function of a herbal with that of a chemical text, it spread the view of the author that distilled remedies were far more potent than the herbs themselves.[9] In this work a wealth of woodcuts illustrate the various types of distillatory apparatus, which were to change little under the Paracelsians. The tradition of medieval alchemy was continued also in a translation of Arnold of Villanova's *Here is a newe boke, called the defence of age and recovery of youth* (1540). In this tract the medical virtues of gold are extolled and wine is called the "quintessence".[10]

Thomas Raynalde's *Compendious declaration of the vertues of a Lateli inuented oile* (Venice, 1551) was an early monograph on a chemical remedy, but it is not until we reach Gesner's *Treasure of Euonymus* (1559) that we have come to the brink of chemical therapy in England. Gesner wrote that the "waters and oyles secreate by the singuler industrie and wit of Chymists, are of most great vertues",[11] but he explained that some physicians rightly held them in contempt because they had been incorrectly prepared in the past.[12] Those who ascribed the introduction of this art to Brunschwig were in error according to Gesner, and his authorities include Dioscorides, Geber, Arnold of Villanova, Ramon Lull, and John of Rupescissa, with the notable omission of Hippocrates and Galen.[13] One whole section of this recipe book is devoted to metallic concoctions, some of which were prepared in the form of precipitates.[14] Despite this aspect of the work, there is no indication that the author desired to overturn the time-honored medical authorities. In fact, in his few references to Paracelsus, Gesner complained bitterly that the Swiss reformer had "condemned Galen, Hippocrates, and all the ancient doctors. . . . I heard that he accomplished nothing worthwhile, indeed, rather he was an impostor. . . ."[15] Although Gesner had an obvious dislike of Paracelsus, he was still forced to admit "that many were cured by him in desperate illnesses and that malignant ulcers were healed by him easily".[16] The veneration in which Gesner was held by most Elizabethan scholars made his approval of chemical medicines of the utmost importance in their gradual acceptance.

A primary concern of the Elizabethan physicians and their Royal College was to rid the realm of the "empiricks and mechanicks": old women who sold potions to their neighbors, people who honestly believed that they had a divine power of healing, and out-and-out quacks. John Caius summed up the situation in his *Counseill against the Sweat* (1552) when he warned against the

simple women, carpenters, pewterers, brasiers, sopeballsellers, pulters, hostellers, painters, apotecaries (otherwise then for their drogges,) auaunters thē selues to come from Pole, Constantinople, Italie, Almaine, Spaine, Fraunce, Grece and Turkie, Inde, Egipt or Jury: from ye seruice of Emperoures, kinges & quienes, promising helpe of al diseases, yea uncurable, with one or twoo drinckes, by waters sixe monethes in continualle distillinge, by Aurum potabile, or quintessence, by drynckes of great and hygh prices, as though thei were made of the sũne, moone, or sterres, by blessynges and Blowinges, Hipocriticalle prayenges, and foolysh smokynges of shirtes Smockes and kerchieffes, wyth suche others theire phantasies, and mockeryes, meaninge nothinge els but to abuse your light belieue, and scorne you behind your backes with their medicines (so filthie, that I am ashamed to name them) for your single wit and simple belief, in trusting thẽ most, whiche you knowe not at al, and understãd least. . . .[17]

In 1565 John Hall wrote *A Most excellent and learned woorke of Chirurgerie para Lanfranci* to which was appended his *historical expostulation . . . against the beastly abusers, both of Chyurgerie and Physicke in our tyme* in which he condemned all quacks and empirics. But although a confirmed traditionalist, Hall made no attack on the new medicine, and instead railed at the ignorant men and women who "forsake their handie craftes, and for filthie lucre abuse phisicke, and chirurgerie".[18] Similarly the *Detection and Querimonie of the daily enormities and abuses committed in physik* of John Securis in 1566 is violent in its treatment of the empirics. There is no reason to believe that any of these attacks were aimed at Paracelsians. But since the quacks obviously did employ chemically prepared potions, it later became easy enough for their enemies to condemn all chemical remedies simply by not distinguishing between the true spagyrists and these men. Thomas Nashe (1594) describes the technique employed by one "Paracelsian" empiric in his *Terrors of the Night*. Here he tells of a needy gallant who victimized a nobleman by working hand in hand with a dishonest druggist. To begin with, this rascal visited his wealthy friend to whom he spoke highly of his new physician, and commented

upon euerie glasse and violl that he hath, rayleth on our Galenists, and calls them dull gardners and haymakers in a mans belly, compares them to dogs, who when they are sick eate grasse, and saies they are no better than pack or malthorses, who if a man should knock out their brains will not goe out of the beaten high way, whereas his horsleach will leap ouver the hedge & ditch of a thousand Dioscorides and Hippocrates and giue a man twentie poysons in one, but he would restore him to perfit health. With this strange tale the Noble-man inflamed, desires to bee acquainted with him: what does me he, but goes immediately and breaks with this mountebanke, telling him if he will diuide his gains with him, he will bring him in custome with such and such States, and he shall bee countenanst in the Court as he wold desire. The hungrie druggier, ambitious after preferment, agrees to any thing, and to Court he goes; where being come to enterview, hee speaks nothing but broken English like a French Doctor pretĕding to haue forgottĕ his naturall tung by trauell, when he hath neuer been farther than either the Lowe Countries or Ireland, inforced thether to flye either for getting a maid with child, or marrying two wiues. Sufficeth he set a good face on it, & will sweare he can extract a better Balsamum out of a chip than the balm of Iudaea: yea, all receipts and authors you can name he syllogizeth of, & makes a pish at in comparison of them he hath seen and read: whose names if you aske, he claps you in the mouth with halfe a dozen spruce titles, neuer til he invĕted them heard of by any Christian. But this is most certaine, if he be of any sect, he is a mettlebruing Paracelsian, hauing not past one or two Probatums for al diseases. But case he be called to practise, hee excuseth it by great cures he hath in hand, & will not encounter an infirmity but in the declining, that his credit may be more autĕtical or els when by some secret intelligence hee is throughlie instructed of the whole processe of his unrecouerable extremitie, he comes grauely marching like a iudge and giues a peremptorie sentence of death: whereby he is accounted a Prophet of deepe prescience.[19]

With such practices being called "Paracelsian" there is little wonder that the term came to have a bad meaning with many people.

The First Accounts

The earliest references to Paracelsus by English authors occur in works dealing with mineral waters. The first of these is a tract describing the waters at Bath by William Turner, a physician and minister, who was forced to flee England during the later years of Henry VIII, and again during the reign of Mary, because of his strong Calvinist leanings. While in Germany he became a friend of Gesner and evidently at the same time learned of the interest of Paracelsus in medicinal waters. As a result he listed Paracelsus as an authority, but he did not give any personal opinion of his work.[20] This treatise was written at

Basel in 1557 and printed in English in 1562, then reprinted in 1568, and often thereafter.

One finds Paracelsus listed again, this time as an authority on surgery, by William Bullein in 1562.[21] Ten years later John Jones (a Cambridge M.D.) wrote on the baths at Buckstones and here he refers disdainfully to the Paracelsian "fyrework of three beginnings, of salt, Brimstone, and quicksilver".[22] Two years later he published his translation of *Galens Bookes of Elementes*. The title page states that this is also a refutation of Paracelsian doctrine, but nowhere in the work is there any amplification of this promise.[23] He slightingly referred again to Paracelsus in his *The Arte . . . of preseruing Bodie and Soule in Healthe* in 1579 and stated that these teachings had been satisfactorily refuted in Latin by Thomas Erastus and in English by one Kinder in a work noted in the margin as *De part. hom.* Outside of this single reference there seems to be no further trace of this work of Kinder, which may have been the first full-fledged attack by an Englishman on Paracelsian thought.[24]

More interesting is a reference to Paracelsus made by the well-known Elizabethan surgeon, George Baker (1540–1600). In 1574, in his preface to a tract, which placed side by side his translations of a monograph on a Spanish chemical oil and the third book of Galen, he compared Paracelsus unfavorably with Galen and cited Erastus as his source.[25] Baker's view is of considerable importance, for although he was a firm supporter of Galen and the rest of the ancients, he was at the same time one of the earliest advocates of the use of chemical therapy. As he later became an ordinary surgeon to Queen Elizabeth and master of the Barber-Surgeons' Company (1597), his views were to carry considerable weight. But by taking his cue from Gesner and the medieval alchemists who sought no quarrel with the ancients, rather than from Paracelsus who seemed to the Elizabethans to want to overturn the whole medical corpus of the past, he outlined the middle path which was eventually to prevail.

This moderate attitude of Baker's is again evident in *The Newe Jewell of Health* (1576). This work was an English translation of the second part of Gesner's *Treasure of Euonymus* (1st ed., Zürich, 1569) made by Thomas Hill.[26] Hill had intended to publish this work but he became seriously ill. Sensing death to be imminent, he bequeathed the manuscript to Baker who saw it through the press and added a preface in which he stated that "the vertues of medicines by Chimicall distillation are made more vailable, better, and of more efficacie than those medicines which are in use and accustomed", but on the other hand, without a knowledge of Galen and Hippocrates the reader would be at a loss to apply properly the remedies in the book.[27]

So we see that, by the end of the 1570s, the few works so far published dealing with chemically prepared medicines were done primarily under the inspiration of Conrad Gesner. With the exception of William Turner's non-committal reference, the citations of Paracelsus had all indicated distrust, the reason for this being that the authors had become acquainted with Paracelsus' work through the refutation of it made by Erastus.

Bostocke's Paracelsian Apology

It was not until 1585 that any Englishman took notice of the comprehensive Paracelsian theories. At that time one R. Bostocke, Esquire, wrote his *Difference betwene the auncient Phisicke . . . and the latter Phisicke.*[28] The author of this work was interested in the theory of Paracelsus rather than in the application of the new chemical remedies. Like John Jones and George Baker, Bostocke was familiar with the work of Thomas Erastus, but unlike them he was appalled by this attack on Paracelsus. Still, he relates that the reason he wrote the book was that

I was the last Parliament time before this that is now sommoned at the table of a reverend Bishoppe of this land, which was not unskilful in Phisicke, in the companie of a Phisition, which inveying against this auncient Phisicke, by the name of Paracelsus his Phisicke, ignorantly attributing to him the first invention thereof, pleased himself and some of his audience in telling that the same Phisicke had no ground nor foundation, neither any being.[29]

This was a new approach in terminology. George Baker and John Hester (whose work will be considered later) had pointed out that the new chemical remedies had in reality an origin earlier than the first years of the current century, but nevertheless they had still considered this as the new "phisicke" in contrast to the old "phisicke" of Galen. Bostocke, on the other hand, considered it his primary aim to point out that iatrochemistry was actually the ancient medicine which after the fall of man had steadily deteriorated until it had reached the depraved state in which Galen offered it. The original chemical physicians were to be sought in a line of sages that ran from Adam through the sons of Seth, Abraham, Moses, Hermes Trismegistus, Thales, Democritus, Pythagoras, and even Hippocrates. Untold secrets were to be discovered in the myths of the sages, but by the time of Plato and Aristotle all this was changing. Bostocke correlated Plato's contempt of Greek physicians with their lack of chemical knowledge, and he treated Aristotle with even more scorn than Galen.[30]

The heathnish Phisicke of Galen doth depende uppon that heathnish Philosophie of Aristotle, (for where the Philosopher endeth, there beginneth the Phisition) therfore is that Phisicke as false and iniurious to thine honor and glory, as is the Philosophie.[31]

Thus it was on religious grounds that he rejected Aristotle and Galen when he spoke of "the heathnish Philosophy of Aristotle, which admitteth nothing, that cannot be demonstrated".[32] Continuing his historical treatment, Bostocke granted merit in the period up to the sixteenth century only to the Alexandrian alchemists, the Arabian adepts, and a handful of Western chemists and alchemists of the late middle ages such as George Ripley.

Hence, to Bostocke, the reform of Paracelsus was just a

purification of medicine, much as his age saw the restoration of other fields of discipline to their pristine purity. He explained that Paracelsus

was not the author and inventour of this arte as the followers of the Ethnickes phisicke doe imagine, as by the former writers may appeare, no more then Wicklife, Luther, Oecolãpadius, Swinglius, Calvin &c. were the Author and inventors of the Gospell and religion in Christes Church, when they restored it to his puritie, according to Gods word, and disclosed, opened and expelled the Clowdes of the Romish religion, which long time had shadowed and darkened the trueth of the worde of God. And no more then Nicholaus Copernicus, which lived at the time of this Paracelsus, and restored to us the place of the starres according to the trueth, as experience and true observation doth teach is to be called the author and inventor of the motions of the stars, which long before were taught by Ptolemeus Rules Astronomicall, and Tables for Motions and Places of the starres and by others, whose Tables of Motions of the starres by long excesse of time grewe to be unperfect (which imperfections by Copernicus his observations were disclosed, opened and brought to their former puritie . . .).[33]

The reference to Copernicus is an early and interesting English notice of this astronomical system, although Bostocke considered the Copernican work to be no more than a restoration of the Ptolemaic star tables.

The religious aspects of the Paracelsian system are of paramount importance to Bostocke, and as the heavenly virtues of chemical remedies are compared with the true doctrine of Christ, so the "corporall and Grosse medicines" of Galen and the common doctor may be likened to the Romish religion which

is mixed with impurities, and standeth in outward ceremonies and traditions, corporal exercises, which be less to the workes of the spirite, whylest it is occupied about them.[34]

But if

The Chymicall Phisition in his Phisicke first and principally respecteth the worde of God, and acknowledgeth it to be his gifte, next he is ruled by experience, that is to say, by the knowledge of the three substanties, whereof eche thing in the great world and man also consisteth, that is to say, by their severall Sal, Sulphur and Mercury, and by their several properties, vertues, and natures, by palpable and visible experience. And when he knoweth the three substanties and all their properties in the great world, then after shall he knowe them in man. For man is Microcosmus for this cause, that hee might have the good and bad sicknesse and health of the great world.[35]

Clearly, then, Bostocke thoroughly accepted the time-honored concept of the macrocosm and the microcosm which was a fundamental part of Paracelsian theory. Also of basic importance to Bostocke were the use of the three principles and the discarding of the traditional humoral system. He explained that

Humors and qualities, to the which the folowers of the Ethnikes doe so much cleaue, and in the which they spende their study and labour, are but onely dead accidents, without power of lyfe. They be conditions, signes, tokens, and as it were onely flowers and colours of diseases and not the very matter, cause, substance, or nature of the disease, they are caused and not the causes. . . .[36] [However] ech member hath his proper humour not like to any of the fower, but according to the cõstitution of the members, and their effect, eche member possesseth his own humor.[37]

Whereas Paracelsus had elaborated on a system of five basic diseases in his *Volumen Paramirum*,[38] Bostocke preferred a variant theory based more rigidly on the three principles.

Therefore there be three generall kinds of diseases, and eche of them haue their especiall sortes of infirmities, as there be sundry sorts of Sal, Sulphur and Mercuri of diuers and sundry natures. There be likewise three kinds of medicine required, and eche kinde of sondry nature to preserue or restore mans body to health.[39]

Diseases were to be cured with a knowledge of the Paracelsian arcana, and by a unitary rather than a dualistic method. In other words, a disease contracted in a lead mine could be cured with a remedy prepared from lead. The dualistic method of the Galenists, on the other hand, indicated a medicine prepared from a substance opposite to that which caused the disease.[40]

The new medicine was introducing a new system of nomenclature to replace the senseless names of diseases employed by the Galenists.[41] Now an attempt was made to name the disease on the basis of the principle that was its cause. "Anatomy" also was given a new meaning:

he that wil be a perfect Phisition, must know eche disease by his right Anatomie, that is to say, by the matter, property and nature of the true substaunce of the disease, as which of the three substaunces have broken unitie, and not by the signe of it. . . . For the right Anatomy consisteth not in cutting of the body, but in the knowledge of the Amitie, concord and nature of all naturall externe things, with man, which doe agree, imbrace and receave eche other, and concord together in mutual agreement, in vertue, power, propertie and essence, to defend nature.[42]

And again, the chemical surgeon avoids the knife and instead works with "oyles and Balmes to pacifie nature, and to keep the wounde defended from accidents, and to leave the cure to nature which is able then to be its own surgeon".[43]

In regard to the relation of chemistry to medicine, Bostocke was unequivocal, for at the opening of the volume he stated that

The true and auncient phisicke which consisteth in the searching out of the secretes of Nature, whose study & uses doth flowe out of the Fountaines of Nature, and is collected out of the Mathematicall and supernaturall precepts, the exercise whereof is Mechanicall, and to be accomplished with labor, is part of Cabala, and is called by auncient name Ars sacra, or magna, & sacra scientia, or Chymia, or Chemeia, or Alchimia, & mystica & by some of late Spagirica ars.[44]

And although he said that "the Chymicall Philosopher layeth the foundation of his Philosophie in Gods booke",[45] he was well aware that according to Paracelsus the Creation could be interpreted as nothing but a divine chemical separation.[46]

But those who were thinking they might make gold by this process were greatly deceived, for the alchemists were really discussing the preparation of medicines which would cure all bodily ills, and not secret recipes for the transmutation of the base metals, as it appeared on the surface. The occult language of the ancient alchemists was explained by Bostocke:

because Secretes are to be reveyled onely to the Godly, and unto the children of doctrine and knowledge, and unto the wise, therefore they did write unto such, that the secrets might be hidden from the ungodly, foolish, slouthful and unthankefull hypocrites, whereby the wise and diligent with travayle and labour might attaine to the understanding thereof, as one of them sayde, it is not meete to provide for a man a Pigion and to rost it for him and also to put it unto his mouth or chawe it for him.[47]

Fully aware that the Paracelsians were being castigated on the Continent for their use of strong inorganic compounds as medicines, Bostocke laid heavy emphasis upon the purification of the chemical remedies and their use in small quantities.[48] Furthermore, he contrasted the chemical physician who carefully extracted the essence of metals by means of his art with the traditionalist who used

Golde, and steale in Drink or Brothe, . . .[and gave] Golde beaten into fine leaves in medicine, and . . . [used] pearls and Precious stones (which be Mynerals also) in power (which is their body) for medicin and sometimes the very bodies of some Mettals: which is contrary to the rules of this auncient Chymycall Phisicke, and thinke they doe much good therewith.[49]

But those who complained that the chemical physicians—or spagyrists—only dealt with mineral remedies were in the wrong, for Bostocke pointed out that herbs and plants formed a valuable part of the physicians' cures just as long as they were treated chemically before being administered to the patient.[50] The chemical physician is also warned not to experiment on men; instead he should learn the cause of the disease through the macrocosm and then apply it to his patient. This again was one of the chief points of attack on the Paracelsians on the Continent, and Bostocke put the matter in these words:

So in ministering of medicines, he willeth them not to minister, before they know the cause and nature of the disease, and what and how much it wanteth of his proper nature, and what and how much it hath gotten of an other nature. For *incognita causa, a casu procedit cura*, to the knowledge whereof wee ought to come, as the Alkimistes doe come to the knowledge of the body that is to them unknowne, and not by trying of the medicine in man.[51]

Finally, Bostocke took up certain objections which had been specifically raised to Paracelsus and his works. This was necessary, for he held that, beyond the appeal first to Holy Scripture and then to personal experience, the physician who

listeth to leane to Bookes . . . [should] learne of those Bookes which Paracelsus hath most Godly and learnedly expressed in his Labyrinth. In comparison of which al other Aucthorities in those matters are small or none.[52]

Thus Erastus had accused him of "Heresie, conjurations, lacke of learning, as also hurt and danger of mynerall medicines and obscuritie of writyng". The reasons for the obscurity and the true explanation of mineral remedies have already been dealt with, and as for the connection with the magical arts,

Paracelsus excludeth from the true, pure, and auncient Magike, and from his coelestiall medicine, all Nigromancie, Sorcery, Ceremonies, Coniurations, and all maner of invocations of devilles, Demones & evill spirits: And he giveth an especiall charge that this Arte be onely used to doe good, and not to the prejudice nor hurt of any bodie and that it be done without Ceremonies, Coniurations, Invocations, Consecrations, Blessinges, and all maner superstytion whereby it becometh ungodly.[53]

This is a not unusual defence of natural magic.

To those who complained that the works of Paracelsus lacked any logical method, Bostocke replied that this was a lie in most cases, but that a lack of method was intentional in some other cases in which the great master had planned to restrict his choicest secrets only to the initiated.[54] And to those who complained that Paracelsus wrote only in German and knew no Latin, he answered that this too was an untruth as some of his works were in Latin.[55] Yet although all other objections could be swept away, Paracelsus' reputation as a drunkard remained to trouble Bostocke's essentially Puritan mind. Compromising, by attributing this fault less to the man than to the habit of his country, he suggested that "the doctrine bee tried by the worke and successe, not by their faultes in their lives".[56]

In a bid for a revision of the medical curriculum in the universities, Bostocke complained that

in the scholes nothing may be received nor allowed that savoreth not of Aristotle, Gallen, Avicen, and other Ethnickes, whereby the yong beginners are either not acquainted with this doctrine, or els it is brought into hatred with them . . . likewise the Galenists be so armed and defended by the protection, priviledges and authoritie of Princes, that nothing can be allowed that they disalowe, and nothing may bee received that agreeth not with their pleasures and doctrine,[57]

and he concluded that if it were lawful for men to study both sides of the question the Paracelsian doctrines would triumph.

Bostocke was the only English author in the sixteenth century who was interested more in Paracelsian theory than in its practice. Others might invoke Paracelsian support for the introduction of chemical remedies, but even here the trend was more to seek precedent in the recipe books of Gesner and Fioravanti edited by George Baker and John Hester. But by Bostocke we are provided with a small compendium of Paracelsian doctrine much as the Swiss reformer originally presented it, a mixture of grandiose theory and valuable reform.

There is, however, no indication that anyone was impressed or even interested in his work. The fact that he was not a physician and only signed his work with his initials did not lend conviction to his account. In the following year (1586) Bostocke's work was referred to by the equally unknown I.W. in a short defence of chemical medicines.[58] This work too is an apology for the Paracelsians, but on a much lower level. I.W. says that his only desire is to convert the reader to the Paracelsian medical preparations, and he implies that a discussion of the deeper aspects of their theory and their relation to the macrocosm and the microcosm will be offered in the author's forthcoming *Anatomy of Death*. (I have been unable to find any reference to the existence of this latter work.) He passes over the question of the antiquity of the "new sect", and merely refers the reader to the recent work of "Master B". He insists on the need in chemistry to separate the pure from the gross parts of the medicines, and explains that the Galenic remedies often cause harmful results because the impure parts of the medicine gain control of the body. I.W. defended Paracelsus by showing that the Swiss physician did write in Latin as well as German, and in regard to his supposed heresy and conjury I.W. referred the reader to Paracelsus' *De occulta Philosophia* and *De Magia*. The excessive drinking of his idol remained to trouble him also, and I.W. decided that Paracelsus had to spend so much time at his hot furnaces distilling and subliming that he had to drink to cool off. "But that hee was a drunkard, or tooke more than he could beare away, you cannot proove, neither doo his workes declare." Many pages of this unnumbered tract deal with a discussion of specific remedies, but the author's failure to discuss Paracelsian theory in detail is to be regretted.

Paracelsus and the English Medical Profession 1580–1600

Although Bostocke's tract stands as the single example of an English exposition of Paracelsian theory prior to 1600, treatises devoted to the new chemical medicines began to be published in ever-increasing numbers. The popularity of these remedies in the mid-1570s is attested by George Baker, who listed the chemical practitioners in London to whom the physician or surgeon could turn with confidence should he desire any of the new medicines. Baker recommended:

one mayster Kemech an Englishe man dwelling in Lothburie, another mayster Geffroy, a French man dwelling in Crouched friers, men of singular knowledge that waye, another named John Hester dwelling on Powle's wharfe, the which is a paynfull traveyler in those matters, as I by proofe have seene and used of their medicines to the furtheraunce of my Pacients healthes.[59]

Little is known of Kemech or Geffroy, but John Hester was to become one of the leading popularizers of the new medicine in this period. Of his life relatively little has come to light, but in his preface to the second part of his *Secrets of Physick and Philosophy* he tells us that as a youth he hungered to become a person "such as others would wonder at". He gave up all thoughts of going to Oxford or Cambridge when he reflected on the fact that the academic training would require seven years and an apprenticeship would last at least that long again. Hence, attracted by the study of "mineralls, herbs and flowers", he "vowed to serve and honor them".[60] He was evidently active in London as a distiller no later than the early 1570s, and he was, like Baker, an intimate friend of Thomas Hill. Just as Hill had left his manuscript of *The Newe Jewell* to Baker, so too he had bequeathed to Hester the manuscript of a second work. This was a translation from the Italian chemical physician, Leonardo Fioravanti, titled *A Ioyfull Iewell* (1579). In the preface Hester stated that

that . . . learned yung man Thomas Hill a countrey man of ours, deserveth great praise of us that first translated them [the works of Fioravanti] into our vulgar or English tung, whereby we shalbe partakers of those precious practices as well as the Italians, who had such a care to pleasure this his countrey (beeing prevented by the stroke of death before he could publish them) committed them to my hands, requesting me to set them foorth in print, which I have polished and filed as nye I could, according to the right sence of the Author, with no small travayle, industrye, labour and dilligence, partely to releeve the rich, partely to profit the poore, but cheefely to comfort my whole contrey.[61]

Hester was a practical man and he realized that he could best help the new chemical remedies (and his business) to prosper by acting as propagandist. From the 1570s until his death (*c.* 1593) he continued to pour out a flood of translations. At first he concentrated on Fioravanti's works, but later he turned to other authors such as Duchesne and Hermann and to spurious works by Paracelsus and others. Relatively uninterested in the deeper aspects of Paracelsism, he normally chose works to translate which were short on theory and long on lists of chemical recipes. Provided the tracts had these recipe collections attached to them, he cared little what other theoretical views they put forth. Actually his authors agreed on little more than two specific points in medical reform: the importance of chemical remedies and the need for experimentation. But aside from this, his translations advanced all sides of the views being expressed at that time by the Continental spagyrists. For instance, Duchesne could praise Paracelsus and accept Galen at the same time,[62] while Fioravanti praised hardly anyone but himself.[63] Another author, Barnard G. (Londrada) A. Portu Aquitanus, in his preface to the *One Hundred and Fourteen Experiments of Paracelsus* showed the bitter hatred of some Continental Paracelsians for the Galenists.[64] As Hester was no theorist, he himself made no mention of the three principles of Paracelsus, and his prefaces note no alarm when Duchesne and Fioravanti continue to use the old system of the four elements and their corresponding humors. Duchesne had developed an independent system, relating the elements and the principles, which was to be offered to English readers in a translation by Thomas Tymme in 1605, but there was no hint of this theory in Hester's translations.[65]

In his support for the new medicines Hester particularly stressed the fact that there were new diseases for which the ancient medicine had no cure—and the most notorious of these were the venereal diseases. In his preface to Hermann's *Treatise teaching howe to cure the French-Pockes . . . Drawen out of that learned Doctor and Prince of Phisitions, Theophrastus Paracelsus* (1590), Hester attacked Galen and Hippocrates and those who tried to apply their methods to diseases they never knew of.

Now that the diseases of the French Pocks was neyther knowne to them, nor to theyr successors for many yeeres . . . is a matter so far out of question, that it refuseth all shew of disputation, and therefore as this latter age of ours sustaineth the scourge thereof, a iust whyp of our lycentiousness, so let it (if ther be any to be had) carry the credite of the cure, as some rewarde to some mens industries.[66]

The remedies suggested were guaiac wood (actually opposed by Paracelsus) and mercury compounds.

Surgical reform was suggested in the translation of a work in which Duchesne deplored the barbaric method of cauterizing the stump of an amputated limb with boiling oils, and suggested instead that wounds would be healed much faster and more effectively by the constant application of warm running water.[67] The same author also pointed out that the chemical approach to "physicke" was not something new with Paracelsus, but rather was an ancient art.[68]

Although Hester believed that alchemy was a necessary handmaiden to medicine, he had no delusions that he could employ it to transmute the base metals into gold:

for it seemeth unreasonable that a man in so short time should doe that thing which nature doth in many yeares. And that men should presume to doe that which God doth only himself, and not any of his creatures. . . . But wee will leave the answer to those that take it to be done.[69]

However, despite this personal opinion, he had no qualms about offering to the reader Duchesne's twelve steps leading to trans-mutation.[70]

Warning his reader against "cut rate druggists", Hester asked him to choose his pharmacist with care, at the same time advertising his own medicines.[71] And it was customary for him to close each of his translations with something similar to that which he inserted as the closing words of Fioravanti's *Short Discourse uppon Chirurgerie* (1580):

If any be disposed to have any of these aforesayd compositions redy made, for the most part he may have them at Paules Wharfe, by one Iohn Hester practisioner in the Arte of distilliations, at the signe of the Furnaises.[72]

Hester's many translations were undoubtedly of the greatest importance in the introduction of chemical remedies into

England, and through them many English physicians must have become aware for the first time of the different aspects of the new movement on the Continent. His work was much less important for the spread of Paracelsian thought in England, for although he translated a few minor works or extracts from the Swiss reformer, he instinctively chose items which were rich in recipes and conscientiously avoided the more obscure and less profitable works which set forth the Paracelsian theories. But even so, Hester's translations were the only English works ascribed to Paracelsus until the middle of the next century, when the English phase of the Paracelsian conflict reached its peak. For this very reason, these translations were reprinted as there was nothing else available. Hence, the *One Hundred and Fourteen Experiments* was reprinted in 1652, and the *Keys of Philosophie* of 1575 was reissued in 1633 as the *Secrets of Physick*—still with the translator's offer to prepare any of the medicines described at a reasonable fee, even though he had been dead for forty years.[73]

No other apothecary or distiller was as outspoken in his praise of chemistry as Hester, but the early and non-controversial acceptance of chemical *remedies* may be seen in the works of the English surgeons and physicians.[74] George Baker, master of the Company of Barber-Surgeons in 1597, had been one of the first to promote such remedies in the 1570s, and although he had no love for Paracelsus, many of his colleagues borrowed freely from the specifically Paracelsian remedies. One of the most notable instances of this is the *Antidotarie* of the famous English surgeon John Banister (1589). In this collection of cures for various wounds, Banister cited Paracelsus and his disciples Duchesne and Thurneisser no less than thirty-five times.[75] Nicholas Gyer, noting the dangers resultant from blood letting performed by unskilled lancers, suggested that such men should be treated as witches; but despite this drastic attitude he did not suggest that there was any relation between quacks and Paracelsians.[76]

William Clowes was another noted Elizabethan surgeon. In a work published by him in 1579 he attacked an empiric by the name of Valentine Razewarme of "Smalcald" as a "bungling botcher", but he made no reference to him as a Paracelsian.[77] It was only a few years later that Clowes first took notice of Paracelsus in his writings, and when he did, he was most careful to distinguish between the "proud pratling Paracelsian", and "the good workes of the right Paracelsian".[78] He made the same distinction between the true and the false Paracelsians in his *Prooued practise for all young Chirurgians* (1588),[79] and in his preface to Peter Lowe's *Whole Course of Chirurgerie* (1597) he referred warmly to "Paracelsus and other learned writers".[80] In his last publication (1602) Clowes stated his position clearly in regard to Paracelsus when he wrote that

I must confesse his Doctrine hath a more pregnant sence then my wit or reach is able to construe: onely this I can say by experience, that I haue practised certaine of his inuentions Chirurgicall, the which I haue found to be singular good, & worthy of great commendations. How be it, much strife I know there is betwen the Galenistes and the Paracelsians, as was in times past betweene Aiax and Ulisses, for Achilles Armour. Notwithstanding, for my part I will heere set up my rest and contentation, how impertinent and unseemely so euer it make shew: That is to say, if I find (eyther by reason or experience) any thing that may be to the good of the Patients, and better increase of my knowledge & skil in the Arte of Chirurgery, be it eyther in Galen or Paracelsus; yea, Turke, Iewe, or any other infidell: I will not refuse it, but be thankfull to God for the same.[81]

This attitude of Clowes is indeed a laudable one, yet it may be seen simply as an approval of chemical therapy. If Clowes accepted the work of Paracelsus in this field, he at the same time made it perfectly clear that he did not understand his philosophical thought.

One could hardly have expected there to be any real enthusiasm for the chemical remedies among the members of the Royal College of Physicians, since most of these men had been brought up in the traditional training based on the ancients:

but here, too, a surprising moderation is evident. In 1585 the members proposed to publish an official pharmacopoeia, and one of the sections of the work was to be devoted to chemical medicines. Although the work was never printed, it is interesting that four years later separate committees were set up to prepare the various sections.[82] Among the three physicians put in charge of the section on chemical medicines was Thomas Moffett, whose opinions on chemistry were already well known through his tract *De Jure et Praestantia Chemicorum Medicamentorum* (1584). Moffett (1553–1604) had studied under John Caius and Thomas Lorkin at Caius College and then gone abroad, reading medicine under Plater and Zwinger at Basel and obtaining his M.D. in 1578. During his period at Basel and in the following four years when he traveled through Italy and Germany, he adopted the Paracelsian system of medicine. On his return to England in 1582 he incorporated M.D. at Cambridge, and in the summer of that year he journeyed to Denmark, where he became acquainted with Peter Severinus and Tycho Brahe. He was a candidate of the Royal College of Physicians in December 1585, and was elected a fellow and censor of that body in 1588. He was a man who moved in the highest court circles, and among his friends and patients were numbered such Elizabethan worthies as Sir Francis Drake, Walsingham, and the Earl of Essex.[83]

Although Moffett was a Paracelsian, it was not in the highly partisan sense of the word. In the course of his broad medical training he had learned to appreciate the works of the ancient Greek physicians to a somewhat greater extent than had Bostocke, but here again we may note one of the hallmarks of Paracelsism: if any of the Greek physicians were to be studied, it should be Hippocrates and not Galen. Consequently, we find that Moffett published a digest titled *Nosomantica Hippocrates Prognostica* (Frankfort, 1588). He also assembled a work on entomology (largely from a manuscript started by Wotton, Gesner, and Pennius in the 1550s) which was not published until thirty years after his death by his Paracelsian successor, Theodore Turquet de Mayerne.[84] He is credited with several other works, but the one which concerns us here is his *De Jure et Praestantia Chemicorum Medicamentorum* which was completed in 1584 in London and first published at Frankfort in the same year. Although no English edition appeared, it seems to have been fairly popular on the Continent where it was reprinted at Nassau in 1602 and later included in the first volume of Zetzner's *Theatrum Chemicum*.

This tract, which comprises only forty-four pages in the 1659 edition, is composed of some prefatory remarks, a dialogue between two physicians identified only as Philerastus (Phil-Erastus) and Chemista, and five appended letters dealing with various aspects of the new medicine.[85] The work concentrates on the defence of chemical remedies, but the author's know-ledge of Paracelsian dogma is evident throughout. Evidently inspired to write it after his trip to Denmark, he dedicated it to his new-found friend Peter Severinus, the chief physician to King Frederick of Denmark and one of the most important of the Continental Paracelsians. In the dedicatory letter he also sent his regards to Tycho Brahe.

Moffett begins by admitting that

Many are beginning to hold chemistry in such distaste that they are horrified by the very name itself, . . . while others praise chemical remedies loudly, but so often by their own negligence has Vulcan permitted faults, that they abandon the art or expose to ridicule their demonstrations.[86]

Indeed, in the dialogue, Philerastus complains that the rumor has reached him that "chemical remedies are by far the most dangerous, and that various illnesses have been carried to excessive violence in applying them".[87] Chemista replies by means of an explanation of where chemical remedies are being used and by whom. He cites the ancients, the Arabs, and the men of his own day, among whom he singles out "that upright Gesner of blessed memory". After this imposing list of authorities he speaks in awe of their "golden preparations of metals and minerals" and concludes that

> if you wish to stand your ground on the judgment of the ancients or of the more recent writers, it would have to be conceded that the mineral and metallic remedies not only should merit their place with the doctors, but that they should even be preferred.[88]

In regard to the relation of the heavenly bodies to earthly ones, Moffett is uncompromising, for when Philerastus wants to know just what the Zodiac is, Chemista replies that

> the signs of animals are not preserved for those phantasms of the astrologers, but rather for true and vital matters; for I believe that there is a double life in these animals; one of which is in them themselves, the other which operates in us; and when the first passes away, the second gains control; and the remedy of death offers to the body an alteration, much as food offers to it nutrition.[89]

Indeed, all earthly matter is connected with the divine beings:

> For in truth there is as much virtue in us as there is God in us, as much wickedness as there is the devil; as much reason as there is the angels; as much motion and sense of choice as there is in us the brutes; as much growth as there is of plants; and there is as much salt, sulphur and mercury as there is of mineral matter.[90]

The Paracelsian three principles play a prominent role in Moffett's tract, and he clearly shows his irritation at the growing number of independent systems of elemental theory put forth by various Continental authors when he complains that

> Some wish that there should be but one element, while others think there are many, and some even think they are infinite, innumerable and immovable: these assert that there are two, those three, some others say four, while others still demand eight.[91]

Actually Moffett appealed for the acceptance of the three principles not through blind belief, but rather through experiment, for:

> Henceforth let us say that the body of men consists of sulphur, mercury, and salt alone, not because we know this as perfectly as Adam, but because

the resolution of all kinds of natural as well as artificial bodies shows it to be so.[92]

The theory of the principles is developed in far more detail when Moffett avers that

Paracelsus and other well known chemists, who have drawn so much light from God, have shown that the principal matter of man has come forth from the earth where it was concealed; for they have dissected its veins with continual and enormous labor, they have opened the viscera, they have broken the bones, they have dissolved the marrow, indeed, they have not moved a stone without at that very place examining it. At length, with the benefit of Pyrotechny and Alchemy, and by their long and almost Herculean labors, they have found nothing simple in the earth except the vaporous, the inflammable, and the fixed: nothing mixed which was not composed out of the same simples. On which account they are resolved that man also is of a doubly principled nature, the one being volatile, and the other fixed. The volatile in turn has a duplex nature: the first vaporous, which is called mercury, the second inflammable, which has obtained the name of sulphur. Mercury is the vaporous principle of the body: by itself a boundless, humid, liquid vehicle of natural balsam: combining sulphur with salt is like incorporating water with sand to a calx. Sulphur is the inflammable principle of a body, fatty, light, uniform, a fomentation of vital balsam. Salt truly is the fixed principle of a body, weighty, solid, and uniting the greatest strength, yielding neither to iron nor fire.[93]

At the end of this dialogue Philerastus admitted his defeat and Chemista christened him Philalethes.

The final part of the tract consists of five letters from Chemista, four of which are to his disciple Philalethes the German and in which he takes up various aspects of the new medicine in somewhat more detail. The one of most interest to us is the letter to Philalethes dated from London on the 4th Cal. of February, 1583, in which he refers to a letter from his imaginary(?) friend complaining about the arguments which were being raised against him by a certain Galenist and his cronies. He is asked for help in replying to these charges, and he gladly obliges. As this letter of his includes specific attacks on Paracelsus it is perhaps worthwhile to quote it at some length. He begins by quoting Philalethes' antagonist to the effect that

"Chemists depart completely from the authority of the medical fathers": but I say that if they should do this in some things, I judge it to be a fair charge: but if truly in all things (as he imagines perfidiously) I consider it to be very unfair. . . .
And he says that chemists are ignorant of all the more refined remedies: that they have not chosen from the Greek authors, that they have scarcely respected the Arabs, but that they have chosen from Paracelsus alone, a drunkard, magician, impostor, beggar, market attender, worker of the hidden arts of heaven and earth, in short, a man hated to the learned . . . I call forth that braggart (the least of all the chemists) into their own arena, and I should fear not at all to debate with him on the subject of the Greeks or Arabs . . . in regard to the faults of Paracelsus . . . Natural cabala, pyrotechny, the exaltation of medicines, the contemplation of physical matters, miraculous invention, the singular ingenuity of Paracelsus; these things delight, captivate, allure and attract chemists; non-natural magic, drunkenness, abusive language, contempt of method, all these things are repudiated by chemists not only in those Greeks and Ethnics, but also in that same Paracelsus. . . .
"Paracelsus was obscure." I confess this and for the sake of it rejoice. But Hippocrates was also most obscure, nor was there ever understanding from Galen unless it was only partly from the words and the rest from feeling.
"He did not know the method." But Hippocrates also did not know it, or at least spurned it. . . .
"Paracelsus often placed contraries as principles and Proteus himself did not differ from himself as much as Paracelsus does from Paracelsus." Actually, unless indulgence be given to this mistaken recollection we shall be forced to admit that Hippocrates differed from himself an infinite number of times. I call to account Cardanus and Rorarius and even Erastus, who have noticed various contradictions of his.

"But Paracelsus was also a magician and an impostor who had dealings with demons. He so indulged in drunkenness that he drank for whole days and nights with farmers, porters and the lowest type of hangmen." Which things I might concede to be all true: however, the defenders of Galenic medicine have similar faults and even worse ones by far [at this point he goes into the details of an abortion Hippocrates performed on a dancing girl and the impiety of Galen]. Now I come to the ignorance of Paracelsus in learned and humane letters: and although I might stain him somewhat, still I cannot concede as much as this man wishes. For he knew the Galenic doctrine, he has commented on Hippocrates: he examined the Arabs, he delivered a book on tartar with a surgery to some schools in Latin letters, and he lectured publicly in the Academy at Basel. It is true that "Paracelsus spoke a great deal in German," but in the same manner Hippocrates spoke Greek as naturally both of them spoke their native tongues. Is this worthy of reprehension in Paracelsus and to be passed over in Hippocrates, Aetius, Actuarius, Galen and Moschion? . . .

"Paracelsus was ignorant of Logic, Physics, Astrology, and Geometry." And what might I say of those Galenic sectarians of whom no one could define their art so that either it might satisfy others or themselves? For this one contends it to be an art, that one a science: a third, both of these and neither: the fourth defines it from its end: the fifth from the work: the sixth from the occurrences: the seventh says that "Medicine is an art of curing and bringing health": but he adds to it "in the human body", as if truly the nature and name of medicine was more fitting to this end than to the curing of plants, or even cattle . . . [he concludes by ridiculing the predictions of the astrologers and the] ignorance of the Geometers is so marked that they assert their defence of the revolution of the earth and seas with preciseness, however, as to how much difference separates London from the little town of Iselinus, they know equally as little. But although the Galenist was not ashamed to call Paracelsus the object of hatred of heaven and earth, it would now seem that the shame has lept across from one party to the other.[94]

It is evident that the Royal College of Physicians had at least one Paracelsian in its midst, and even if this tract was not printed in England, Moffett must have made his views known to his colleagues. It was probably largely due to his efforts that when the College proposed to issue a pharmacopoeia in the mid-1580s it was planned to include a section on chemical remedies.[95] Although this was never printed, it is significant in showing that the members of the College were not quite as uncompromising in their attitude toward the innovations as might have been expected. Actually, the sources seem to confirm the fact that the Royal College of Physicians at this time had little complaint with the reputable purveyors of the new medicines or the physicians who administered them. The *First Book of the Annals of the Royal College of Physicians* by John Caius and the *Historical Account of the College's proceedings against Empiricks and unlicensed Practisers* (1684) of Dr. Charles Goodall refer often enough to the more obvious quacks who in selling their special brands of *aurum potabile* or quintessences promised cures for all kinds of incurable diseases, but not to men of the stature of Baker and Hester. During the reign of Elizabeth, men such as Simon Forman and Francis Anthony found themselves in trouble more than once for their dangerous and sometimes fatal prescriptions, but sincere practitioners had little to worry about.

A perusal of some of the stock medical works by the traditionalists written during the formative period of this movement in England reveals little alarm at the innovations. It would seem that the average English physician was indifferent rather than hostile to chemical medicines. Thomas Brasbridge's *Poore Mans Jewell* of 1579 contains no mention of them. The same can be said of William Cary's *Farewell to Physicke* of 1583 and Thomas Cogan's *Haven of Health* of 1589. In 1583 Philip Barrough admitted that the empirics had found some useful remedies for the *Morbus Gallicus* in his *Method of Phisicke*, but this was the limit of his knowledge of the new ideas.[96] A more unusual treatment was that given by William Clever in the *Flower of Phisicke* published in 1590. Clever produced a collection of sentences culled from the leading authorities of his day on a variety of medical questions. For the most part these are taken from the ancients, but mingled among the quotations from Galen, Hippocrates, and the others are scattered selections from Paracelsus on human heat, the ministration of medicines, and a variety of other unrelated topics.[97]

The comprehensive tomes of Christopher Wirtzung and Oswald Gaebelkhover were translated in 1598 and 1599, and chemical remedies were to be found in these huge works which must have inspired confidence because of their bulk if for no other reason.[98] The Baker-Hill translation of *The Newe Jewell of Health* reappeared with a revised title, *The Practise of the new and old phisicke* (1599) and a symbolical engraving of "Alchymia" on the title page. Baker also contributed an introductory letter to John Gerarde's famed *Herball* (1597). However, the most interesting aspect of the Gerarde work is another appended letter from Stephen Bredwell who sought to abolish the "pernicious impostures and sophistications" of the Paracelsians, but at the same time suggested the establishment of a chemical lectureship at the Royal College of Physicians. Converted to, but still somewhat sceptical of, the iatrochemists, this author wrote:

I say in like manner, the art of Chimistrie is in it selfe the most noble instrument of naturall knowledges; but through the ignoraunce and impietie, partly of those that most audaciously professe it without skill and partly of them that impudently condemne that they knowe not, it is of all others most basely despised and scornfully reiected.[99]

Another member of the College, Francis Herring, entered the lists of the anti-Paracelsians shortly after the turn of the century. In 1602 he translated the *Anatomyes of the True Physician and Counterfeit Mountebank* in which he attacked Paracelsus, and two years later he set forth his views again in his *A Modest Defence of the Caveat given to the Wearers of impoisoned Amulets, as Preservatives from the Plague*. Admitting that he had wasted some time in the study of the works of Paracelsus, the best he could say for him was that he was "a skilfull Chymicall writer and worker" who should be classified among the "Mechanicks or Empiricks" rather than the learned.[100]

Neither doe I yet denie but that he hath some things of good use. And so had Thessalus that old Bragadochian of Galens time, and Fioravantus that notorious Empiricke & Impostor of our time, who was banished Venice, but those mixed with so much vanitie, pride and insolencie as marreth all. . . . I have often marvelled how any man of wisdome and modestie, seeing the incredible insolencie and impudencie, the intollerable vanitie and follie, the ridiculous and childish crakings and vantings of Paracelsus, should once commend him without noting his contrary vices, and giving him a dash with a blacke coale.[101]

Herring, although wary of chemical therapy, was not opposed to it as long as it was dissociated from the name and writings of Paracelsus.

The work of John Cotta, a Northampton physician, is of particular interest, for when he published his *Short Discoverie of the Unobserved Dangers of severall sorts of Ignorant and Unconsiderate Practisers of Physicke in England* in 1612, about fifty years had elapsed since John Hall and John Securis had exposed the medical frauds of their day. But for the most part the complaints of the 1560s held good for Jacobean England. The chemical quacks selling all sorts of cure-alls in the form of quintessences and potable gold were perhaps even more active than they had been, but the only mention Cotta makes of Paracelsus is the case of a surgeon who prescribed some "Ladanum pills" of Paracelsus to a patient who forthwith fell into fits and convulsions while the surgeon hurriedly left town.[102] But if he felt that Paracelsus and the Paracelsians could be practically ignored in his treatise, he seems to have classified the chemical physicians as a different group, and he evidently felt that the discussion of chemical therapy had to be treated in more detail. Cotta, like most physicians, seemed to prefer a compromise position with a reliance on the best of both the Galenic and the chemical medicines. He wrote that

The innumerable dissentions amongst the learned concerning the Arabicke and Chymicke remedies at this day infinitely, with opposite and contradictorie writings, and invectives, burthen the whole world.[103]

After summarizing the views of the more obstinate adherents to the Galenic and chemical factions, he explained that

A third and more commendable sort differeth from both these, . . . [and] doth from both draw whatsoever may in either seeme goode or profitable unto health or physicke use: from the Grecian deriving the sound and ancient truth, & from both Greek, Chymicke, or Arabian, borrowing with thankfull diligence any helpfull good to needfull use.[104]

Cotta was a leading authority on witchcraft in the reign of James I, but he seems to have made no connection between the natural magic of the Paracelsians and the black magic of the witches and physician sorcerers whom he cited.

The great majority of English physicians and surgeons had adopted a compromise position by the early years of the new century. They readily accepted those of the new remedies which proved their worth, but very few of them concerned themselves with the deeper and more occult aspects of Paracelsian thought. This is in decided contrast with the Continent, where the theory and practice were generally more closely associated and the conflict between the Galenists and the Paracelsians was often far more bitter.

In England the new chemically prepared remedies had come into use by way of the writings of Brunschwig, Villanova, and especially Gesner. This was an older tradition in which the authors or compilers had not sensed any conflict with Galenic medicine. When these works were translated and published in England, the doctors saw no reason why any controversy should develop and they immediately utilized these cures as auxiliary to the traditional ones. The most important of these chemically oriented formularies were Gesner's compilations, *The Treasure of Euonymus* (1559) and *The Newe Jewell of Health* (1576). The latter had been prepared for the press by a noted surgeon, George Baker, and it is significant that the surgeons along with the pharmacists were among the first converts to the new medicines. But the work of Thomas Moffett and the plans for the pharmacopoeia in 1585 testify to the fact that even in the Royal College of Physicians there was no real opposition to the application of chemistry to medicine.

On the other hand, there was an early distrust of Paracelsian occultism. Most of the early English references to Paracelsus came from authors who had read the work of Erastus refuting him. Neither Bostocke's apology for Paracelsian thought (1585) nor Moffett's plea for Paracelsian medicine (1584) caused any noticeable change in the attitude of the English doctors. John Hester was the only translator of the works of the Continental

Paracelsians prior to 1600. He was primarily interested in the recipe collections of Joseph Duchesne and Leonardo Fioravanti, but he did translate two tracts which were ascribed to Paracelsus. However, these also were devoted to recipes rather than theory, and they were the only tracts in English attributed to Paracelsus until the middle of the next century, when the work of van Helmont brought a new interest in the Paracelsian writings. Thus the compromise position of the late sixteenth-century English physicians and surgeons was to be maintained throughout the first forty years of the seventeenth century.

Notes for Chapter Two

1. George Urdang, "How Chemicals entered the Official Pharmacopoeias", *Wisconsin Academy of Science, Arts and Letters*, *39* (1949), 115–25, also printed in *Arch. Int. d'Hist. des Sci.*, 7 (1954), 303–14, from which all citations will be made. Paul H. Kocher, "Paracelsan Medicine in England (*ca.* 1570–1600)", *J. Hist. Med.*, 2 (1947), 451–80; and "John Hester, Paracelsan (fl. 1576–93)", *Joseph Quincy Adams Memorial Studies*, ed. James G. McManaway, Giles E. Dawson, Edwin E. Willoughby (Washington, 1948), 621–38; *Science and Religion in Elizabethan England* (San Marino, Calif., 1953). See also Robert P. Multhauf, "Medical Chemistry and the Paracelsians", *Bull. Hist. Med.*, *28* (1954), 101–26.
2. Kocher, *Adams Memorial Studies*, 623. See also his discussion on page 472 of his article in *J. Hist. Med.*
3. Urdang, *op. cit.*, 305.
4. Prof. Kocher does distinguish between the work of Gesner and Paracelsus, and he states that Gesner was the "prime mover" of chemical medicine in England in its early stages. Kocher, *J. Hist. Med.*, 2, 455.
5. W. S. C. Copeman, *Doctors and Disease in Tudor Times*, 14.
6. *Ibid.*, 36.
7. John Caius, M.D., *The Works of John Caius, M.D.*, ed. E. S. Roberts (Cambridge, 1912), 5f.
8. In spite of the seeming lack of interest in the Paracelsian controversy on the Continent, some of the new advances did appear in England. Parts of the *De humani corporis fabrica* appeared within a few years after its first edition (1543) under the authorship of Thomas Geminus. Later in the century the surgical advances of Ambroise Paré were made available in England through the works of Thomas Gale and William Clowes. See S. V. Larkey, *Medical Knowledge in Tudor England as Displayed in an Exhibition of Books and Manuscripts* (San Marino, Calif., 1935), 5.

9. Hieronymus Brunschwig, *The vertuose boke of distyllacyon*, . . . tr. L. Andrewe (London, 1527).

10. Arnoldus de Villanova, *Here is a newe boke, called the defence of age and recovery of youth*, tr. J. Drummond (London, 1540), *passim*.

11. Conrad Gesner, *The Treasure of Euonymus: conteyninge the wonderfull hid secretes of nature*, tr. P. Morwyng (London, 1559), 293.

12. *Ibid.*, 412.

13. *Ibid.*, 421.

14. Here we have evidence of the isolation of the products of chemical reactions prior to the time of the late sixteenth-century Paracelsians. For Gesner's place in the history of distillation chemistry see Multhauf, "Significance of Distillation", 341.

15. Conrad Gesner, *Bibliotheca Universalis* (Tiguri, 1545), fol. 614.

16. Thomas Erastus, *Disputationum De Medicina nova Philippi Paracelsi: Pars Prima* (Basel, 1572). From the short essay titled "Conradus Gesnerus Medicus Tigurinus de Theophrasto Paracelso" appended to this work.

17. John Caius, *Counseill against the Sweat* in *Works*; 26 (separate pagination).

18. John Halle, *A most excellent and learned woorke of Chirurgerie* (London, 1565), iiif.

19. Thomas Nashe, *The Terrors of the Night* (London, 1594), sig. E–Eii.

20. William Turner, *A Booke of the natures and properties as well of the bathes in England as of other bathes in Germanye and Italye* (Collen, 1562), fol. iii. In the same year this was also issued with the second part of William Turner's *Herball*. In the 1568 edition of this work the preface is dated March 10, 1557 at Basel.

21. William Bullein, *A Little Dialogue betwene twoo men, the one called Sorenes, and the other Chyrurgi* (London, 1562), fol. v. This work is the second part of *Bulleins Bulwarke of defence against all Sicknes, Sornes and woundes*. . . . Bullein refers to Paracelsus as "Theophrastus Peraselpus".

22. John Jones, *Benefit of the Auncient Bathes of Buckstones* (London, 1572), "To the Reader", fol. ii.

23. John Jones, *Galens Bookes of Elementes* (London, 1574).

24. John Jones, *The Arte and Science of preseruing Bodie and Soule in Healthe, Wisdome, and Catholicke Religion* (London, 1579), 31. See also Kocher, *J. Hist. Med.*, 2 (1947), 467.

25. George Baker, *The composition or making of the moste excellent and pretious Oil called Oleum Magistrale* (London, 1574), quotation from the non-paginated "To the Reader".

26. Conrad Gesner, *The Newe Jewell of Health* (London, 1576), "George Baker to the Reader". See also F. R. Johnson, "Thomas Hill: An Elizabethan Huxley" *Huntington Library Quarterly*, 7 (1944), 109–35.

27. Gesner, *Newe Jewell*, iiif.

28. This work of some 96 unnumbered leaves was attributed to "R. Bostocke, Esq." by Andrew Maunsell in his *The Seconde parte of the Catalogue of English printed Bookes* (London, 1595), 4.

29. R. B., Esq., *The difference betwene the auncient Phisicke . . . and the latter Phisicke* (London, 1585), sig. D i.
30. See R.B.'s historical sections, *ibid.*, Chapters 10–19; sig. Fiiii (r) to Jiii (r).
31. *Ibid.*, The Authors obtestation to almightie God. Sig. A v (v).
32. *Ibid.*, The Authors obtestation to almightie God. Sig. A v (r).
33. *Ibid.*, Chapter 19. Sig. Hvii (v) to Hviii (r).
34. *Ibid.*, Chapter 6. Sig. C viii (v).
35. *Ibid.*, Chapter 8, section 5. Sig. D iiii (v).
36. *Ibid.*, Chapter 5. Sig. C vi (v).
37. *Ibid.*, Chapter 8, section 8. Sig. D viii (r).
38. Henry M. Pachter, *Paracelsus* (New York, 1951), 133–34. See the discussion of the five entia in Chapter 1. For the relationship of the three principles to disease in Paracelsus see Pagel, *Paracelsus*, 133–34.
39. R.B., *op. cit.*, Chapter 4. Sig. C iii (v).
40. *Ibid.*, Chapter 1. Sig. B i to B iii.
41. *Ibid.*, Chapter 8, section 13. Sig. E iiii (v).
42. *Ibid.*, Chapter 5. Sig. C vii (r).
43. *Ibid.*, Chapter 11. Sig. G iii (r).
44. *Ibid.*, Chapter 1. Sig. B i (r).
45. *Ibid.*, Chapter 8. Sig. D iii (r).
46. *Ibid.*, Chapter 21. Sig. K ii (r).
47. *Ibid.*, Chapter 3. Sig. C ii (r).
48. *Ibid.*, Chapter 8, section 15. Sig. E v (v).
49. *Ibid.*, Chapter 8, section 12. Sig. E iv (v).
50. *Ibid.*, Chapter 9. Sig. F i (v).
51. *Ibid.*, Chapter 8, section 19. Sig. E viii (v).
52. *Ibid.*, Chapter 8, section 6. Sig. D vi (r).
53. *Ibid.*, Chapter 24. Sig. L iii (r).
54. *Ibid.*, Chapter 24. Sig. L iv (v).
55. *Ibid.*
56. *Ibid.*
57. *Ibid.*, Chapter 9. Sig. F ii (v).
58. I. W., *The copie of a letter sent by a learned Physician to his friend, wherein are detected the manifold errors used hitherto of the Apothecaries* (London, 1586). This short tract is composed of some 15–20 leaves and is non-paginated.
59. Gesner, *Newe Jewell*, iv.
60. Paracelsus, *The Secrets of Physick and Philosophy* (London, 1633), from the non-paginated "To the Reader". These quotations have also been checked against the 1596 edition of this work titled *The Key of Philosophie*.
61. Leonardo Fioravantie, *A Ioyfull Iewell*, . . . tr. John Hester (London, 1579), sig. A ii.
62. Joseph Quercetanus, *A Breefe Aunswere*, tr. John Hester (London, 1591), fols. 1–4.
63. Leonardo Phioravanti, *A Short Discourse uppon Chirurgerie*, tr. John Hester (London, 1580), sig. ¶ iv. On Fioravanti's references to the "divino" Paracelsus,

see Davide Giordano, *Leonardo Fioravanti Bolognese* (Bologna, 1919), 14, note 1.

64. Leonardo Phioravant, *Three Exact Pieces* [including] *One Hundred and Fourteen Experiments and Cures of the Famous Physition Theophrastus Paracelsus*, tr. John Hester (London, 1652), "An Apologeticall Preface of Mr. B. G. Londrada A. Portu Aquitanus."

65. Joseph Quersitanus, *The Practise of Chymicall, and Hermeticall Physicke, for the preseruation of health*, tr. Th. Timme, Minister, (London, 1605). For an excellent modern appraisal of Duchesne's views on the principles and elements see R. Hooykaas, "Die Elementenlehre der Iatrochemiker", *Janus, 41* (1937), 1–28.

66. Phillippus Hermanus, *An excellent Treatise*, tr. John Hester (London, 1590), preface.

67. Joseph Duchesne, *The Sclopotarie*, tr. John Hester (London, 1590), 31.

68. Quercetanus, *Breefe Aunswere*, fol. 1.

69. Paracelsus, *Secrets of Physicke and Philosophy*, 107.

70. Quercetanus, *Breefe Aunswere*, fols. 17f.

71. Leonardo Phioravanti, *A Compendium of the rationall Secretes . . . of the hidden vertues of sondrie vegitables, animalles, and mineralls*, tr. J. Hester (London, 1582), iiii f.

72. Phioravanti, *Short Discours . . . uppon Chirurgerie*, fol. 64.

73. Paracelsus, *Secrets of Physick and Philosophy*, from the non-paginated "to the Reader".

74. Prof. Kocher has followed in considerable detail the references to Paracelsian remedies in the works of the main surgical authors of this period (Clowes, Banister, Baker, etc.), and he has shown that there was a gradual acceptance of chemical therapy by all of these men whom he calls "the most enterprising and enlightened group of surgeons, or indeed, medical practitioners of any kind in England at that time" (Kocher, *J. Hist. Med.*, 2 (1947), 458). This reconciliation of the English surgeons with chemical remedies eventually led them even to look on Paracelsus kindly, but none of them ever pretended to understand deeper Paracelsian thought. See Kocher, *ibid.*, 466–80 *passim*. The changing views of William Clowes in respect to Paracelsus are sketched later in this chapter.

75. For a fuller description of this work see Kocher, *ibid.*, 466–67. For specific references to Paracelsus see John Banister, *An Antidotarie Chyrurgicall* (London, 1589), 20, 97–99, 103, 107, 135, 136, 296–99.

76. Nicholas Gyer, *The English Phlebotomy* (London, 1592), "The epistle dedicatory". This work is dedicated to Reginald Scot.

77. William Clowes, *A Short and profitable Treatise touching the cure of the disease called Morbus Gallicus by Unctions* (London, 1579), sig. Cii.

78. William Clowes, *A Briefe and necessarie Treatise, touching the cure of the disease called Morbus Gallicus* (London, 1585), fol. 59.

79. William Clowes, *A prooued practise for all young chirurgians, concerning burnings with Gunpowder, and woundes with Gunshot* (London, 1588), "To the Reader".

80. Peter Lowe, *The Whole Course of Chirurgerie* (London, 1597), from the "To the friendlie Reader" by William Clowes.

81. William Clowes, *A Right Frutefull and Approoved Treatise for the Artificiall Cure of that Malady called in Latin Struma* (London, 1602), "Epistle to the Reader".

82. *Pharmacopoeia Londinensis . . . with a Historical Introduction by George Urdang* (Madison, 1944), 11.

83. Sidney Lee, "Thomas Moffett", *Dictionary of National Biography* (1949–50 edition), *13*, 548–50.

84. Thomas Moffett, *Insectorum sive Minimorum Animalium Theatrum . . . ad vivum expressis iconibus super quingentis illustratum* (London, 1634).

85. That Philerastus was not supposed to be a blind follower of the traditionalists is evidenced by the following quotation: "Behold the whole tribe of Athenians and Galenists is among men at least in my opinion like (Napelli?), wolf's bane, chameleons; they gratify the eyes and souls with the elegance of color and splendor, however, they are of no good use." *Theatrum Chemicum*, ed. L. Zetzner (Argentorati, 1659), *1*, 71.

86. *Ibid.*, *1*, 64f.

87. *Ibid.*, *1*, 82.

88. *Ibid.*, *1*, 83.

89. *Ibid.*, *1*, 76.

90. *Ibid.*, *1*, 65.

91. *Ibid.*, *1*, 97.

92. *Ibid.*, *1*, 100. For a similar passage see also *ibid.*, *1*, 95.

93. *Ibid.*, *1*, 101.

94. *Ibid.*, *1*, 89–93.

95. Urdang, *op. cit.*, 306.

96. Philip Barrough, *The Method of Phisicke* (6th ed., London, 1624), 364ff. The first edition appeared in 1583.

97. William Clever, *The Flower of Phisicke* (London, 1590), 48, 76, 93, 103, 109, 118, 126, 129.

98. Oswald Gaebelkhover, *The boock of physicke* (Dorte, 1599). Christopher Wirtzung, *Praxis medicinae universalis, or a generall practise of physicke*, tr. J. Mosan (London, 1598).

99. John Gerarde, *The Herball or Generall Historie of Plantes* (London, 1597), introductory non-paginated leaf titled "To the well affected Reader and peruser of this booke".

100. Francis Herring, Dr. in Physicke, *A Modest Defence of the Caveat given to the Wearers of impoisoned Amulets, as Preservatives from the Plague* (London, 1604), 31–32.

101. *Ibid.*, 32–33.

102. John Cotta, *A Short Discoverie of the Unobserved Dangers of severall sorts of ignorant and Unconsiderate Practisers of Physicke in England* (London, 1612), 37.

103. *Ibid.*, 82.

104. *Ibid.*, 83.

Chapter Three

Paracelsian Thought in England, 1600-1640

B Y the late sixteenth century the Paracelsian cosmology had already attracted an impressive number of Continental adherents. These men postulated a universe all of whose parts were interrelated—and this interrelation was often explained by reference to chemical analogies. Even the divine Creation was compared to a chemical separation in which the four elements—or the three principles—had been separated from the primeval chaos and were in turn further defined into the particulate objects or beings of their proper spheres. Mankind was considered to be an integral part of this alchemical universe and the macrocosm-microcosm analogy was freely employed. Man was united with the great world through many cosmic forces or influences, and as the macrocosm might be explained in chemical terms, so too might man. This Paracelsian system of the world, which represents a fusion of various strains of occult philosophy and a fresh appeal to nature, was closely allied with religion as well. Observation and experimentation were not only possible for man, they were also essential for the devout Christian who sought to learn more of his Creator through His Creation.

Nevertheless, this attempt to combine natural philosophy and religion had proved unpopular with most English physicians in the closing years of the sixteenth century. The earliest printed references to Paracelsus had been derived from the work of Erastus criticizing him, and the works of Bostocke and I.W. giving a fuller explanation of Paracelsian thought saw only single editions. Similarly, the interesting treatment by Thomas Moffett probably remained unknown to most English medical men outside of the Royal College of Physicians since it was never printed in England. This distrust of Paracelsian theory stands in marked contrast with the early and general acceptance of chemically prepared medicines which had been proved useful in combating disease.

Paracelsian Theory in a New Century—The Duchesne Influence

It was a full twenty years after the publication of Bostocke before another work primarily devoted to Paracelsian theory was printed in England. In 1605 Thomas Tymme translated sections of two of the most important theoretical works of Joseph Duchesne (Quercetanus), the *Liber de Priscorum Philosophorum verae medicinae materia* (1603) and the *Ad Veritatem Hermeticae Medicinae ex Hippocratis veterúmque decretis ac Therapeusi* (1604), in his *Practise of Chymicall, and Hermeticall Physicke, for the preservation of Health*. Of Tymme's life we know relatively little. He spent some time at Cambridge, but there is no evidence that he obtained a degree there. In 1566 he became rector of St. Antholin's in London and nine years later he was appointed to the same position at Hasketon in Suffolk.[1] In common with Bostocke, Tymme had no connection with the medical profession. As yet the Paracelsian alchemical cosmology had found no apologist among English physicians. But if we are uncertain as to the exact profession of Bostocke, this is not the case with Tymme, who was a minister well known for his translations and his original works on theology and history. Probably his best-known tract was a popular work of devotion titled *A Siluer Watchbell* which had gone through nineteen editions by 1659. However, despite the fact that his religious and historical works date for the most part from the last quarter of the sixteenth century, his contributions to iatro-chemical thought were written in the early part of the reign of King James I. The first of these was the above-mentioned translation from Duchesne[2]—an author already well known to English readers through John Hester's translations of his pharmaceutical writings—and the second was an original work which strongly reflects the earlier translation, his *Dialogue Philosophicall* (1612).

Tymme was attracted to Paracelsian thought because of its connection with religion. In his dedication to Lord Mountjoy, the Lieutenant-General of Ireland, he stated that "Halchymie should have concurrence and antiquitie with Theologie", since Moses

tels us that the Spirit of God moved upon the water: which was an indigested Chaos or masse created before by God, with confused Earth in mixture: yet by his Halchymicall Extraction, Seperation, Sublimation, and Coniunction, so ordered and conioyned againe, as they are manifestly seene a part and sundered: in Earth, Fyer included, (which is a third Element) and Ayre, [and] (a fourth) in Water. . . .

Therefore it is through the divine alchemy that God operated to create the universe and the beginning of time. Now Tymme accepted both the doctrines of the three principles and the four elements although he seems to have been unsure of their relationship. It is "of these 3. [principles] whatsoeuer is in Nature, hath his original, & is compacted of them, and so mingled with the 4 elements that they make one body". As the Creation was an alchemical process, so too the Last Judgment will be carried out in chemical fashion. Since this is so, only a fool can say "There is no God" and it is the wise man who studies nature through chemistry and learns through separation that salt, sulphur, and mercury are always obtained. In this fact we may

discerne the holy and most glorious Trinitie in the Unitie of one Hupostasis Diuine. For the inuisible things of God (saith the Apostle) that is, his eternal power and God-head, are seene by the creation of the world, being considered in his workes.

The study of chemistry then

is not of that kind which tendeth to vanity and deceit, but rather to profit and to edification, inducing first the knowledge of God, & secondly the way to find out true medicine in his creatures.[3]

The close relation of religion and the study of nature is underscored by Tymme when he states that

The Almighty Creatour of the Heauens and the Earth, (Christian Reader), hath set before our eyes two most principall Bookes: the one of Nature, the other of his written Word. . . . The wisedome of Natures booke men commonly call Naturall Philosophie, which serueth to allure to the contemplation of that great and incomprehensible God, that wee might glorifie him in the greatnesse of his worke. For the ruled motions of the Orbes . . . the connexion, agreement, force, vertue, and beauty of the Elements . . . are so many sundry natures and creatures in the world, are so many interpreters to teach us, that God is the efficient cause of them, and that he is manifested in them, and by them, as their finall cause to whom also they tend.[4]

Indeed we need the book of nature to understand divinity. If man had not sinned, nature itself would have been enough for man's knowledge of his Creator, but since the Fall of man, "God hath given us his sacred Booke, by means whereof, as also by his holy spirit, he communicateth to us as much heauenly light as is needfull for the knowledge of our selues, and of his high Maiestie".[5]

It is evident then that Tymme stood for an alchemical interpretation of the Creation and the Last Judgment, the acceptance of the Aristotelian elements as well as the Paracelsian principles, and the correspondence of the latter with body, soul, and spirit. But above all we see his primary interest in the connection between theology and experimental knowledge—especially the value of the latter in giving us greater knowledge of our Creator.

Because of the considerable influence of the views of Duchesne as expressed here, they call for further analysis. Professor Hooykaas has pointed out that Quercetanus was the first Paracelsian to develop the concept of the "five principles" which was so prevalent among chemists and alchemists in the seventeenth century.[6] Duchesne enunciated this theory in his *Le Grand miroir du Monde* (1584) and later in his *Defensio* (1605) where he insisted that there are but two productive elements, water and earth. He believed that fire should be dropped as an element because it is not mentioned as such in Genesis. Similarly, since "Air is nothing but rarefied water", one could not call that substance elementary either. But besides these two productive elements, he went on to show that salt, sulphur, and mercury are basic to all matter since they may be found in all things.[7] Hence, one might conclude that there are but five true elements or principles: water, earth, salt, sulphur and mercury. There are also other aspects of *Le grand miroir* which arrest our attention since they were to influence the English Paracelsians. For instance, he identified the four elements with specific "demons",[8] he pointed out once more Plato's identification of the traditional elements with the regular solids,[9] and he stressed the dual role of sympathy and antipathy as natural forces.[10] Nearly all of these views were to be adopted later by Robert Fludd, who was by far the foremost English alchemical theorist of the first half of the seventeenth century.

Tymme's translation re-echoed many of these concepts, yet there were certain important modifications and changes of emphasis. In particular, Duchesne's views were set forth in such a manner that his readers were led to believe that he had rejected as elements not both fire and air, but fire alone.

In common with other Paracelsians, Duchesne based his cosmology on the Biblical story of the Creation. After separating Light from Darkness, God is pictured as having separated Waters from Waters—meaning the separation of the *tria prima*: salt, sulphur, and mercury.[11] Duchesne strongly emphasized the three principles and to them he assigned the active qualities, while the passive qualities were reserved for the traditional elements. But what of these passive elements? He stated that fire definitely could not be considered a true element for "wee acknowledge no other Fire then Heauen, & the fiery Region which is called of burning". Indeed,

Wherefore, forsomuch as aier and earth, two extreames, are fitlie ioyned together, by a thyrd, which is water, a meane betweene them both: Aristotle did more than was needefull to appoynt a quaternarie number of elements, out of the quaternary number of the fower qualities, Hote, Colde, Drie, Moyst.[12]

This "argument of the mean" as a proof of three rather than four elements derives ultimately from the *Timaeus* where Plato argued that there must be a third element to join together the two extremes of heavenly fire and the earth beneath.[13] Plato called for a double mean to account for water and air, while the simpler argument of Duchesne was more common in the Renaissance and resulted in a theory of three rather than four elements. This concept was to enjoy considerable popularity in the early seventeenth century. However, it should not be thought that this modification of the element theory was original with Duchesne, since both Paracelsus and Jerome Cardan had affirmed that fire was not a true element.[14] On this point Tymme reflected the views of Duchesne:

In Genesis it is euidently to be seene, that there is made mention of Heauen, Earth and Water onely: but of Fire and Aire, no mention at all, because these two are encluded under the other: as under Heauen, Fire, and under the superious waters, Aire: so that hereby it is plaine, that there is no other fierie element but Heauen.[15]

Since there were now to be only three true elements, there could not be a "Quintessence", a term which would have no meaning. Nevertheless, the concept was maintained in Duchesne's "Quartessence" which was an extraction from the three elements and identified in a medicinal sense with the universal Balsamic medicine.[16] Tymme explained that there is

> a fourth essence, separated out of the more subtill matter and forme of the three elements: which being so separated and extracted, is no other thing but a pure Aetheriall and most simple fire, most perfect, and farre different from the three Elements, as imperfect. . . .[17]

In *Le grand miroir* Duchesne had rejected air as an element since he felt that air is merely rarefied water. But this assertion is not strongly made in *The Practise of Hermeticall Physicke* and the English reader was free to conjecture that Duchesne meant that there were three passive elements to correspond with the three active principles.[18] It should further be noted that even if Duchesne had rejected fire as a true element, he still constantly made use of the four traditional elements. In particular he made a point to pair salt with earth, sulphur with fire, and mercury with water and air. And although Duchesne had argued that "Aristotle did more than was needful to appoynt a quaternarie number of elements", Tymme disagreed. Accepting the fact that the three principles are the basic formed matter of the universe, Tymme still went on to insist that Aristotle did have good "reason to appoint a quaternarie of Elements, according to the number of the foure qualities".[19] However, as with Duchesne, these elements are a secondary form of matter since they are formed of the three principles themselves. For Tymme, fire "is a substance containing in it life and motion or the soule of the elements". Air "is a substance which hath in it the nourishing foment of life, and the spirit of the Elements". To earth he assigned an earthy and watery nature which approximates the *prima materia*. This was for him the body of the elements.[20] Although not spelled out with great clarity, the Duchesne and Tymme accounts here lead to a three principle-three element theory based on the story of Creation in which the three elements are essentially earth, heaven (fire), and water. By water could be understood the terrestrial waters and the "upper" waters (air). Thus, although there are only three true elements, they may be explained in terms of the traditional four.

Duchesne's account of the three principles calls for further study, for he discussed all of nature in terms of triads which could then be equated with the all-important *tria prima*. He stated flatly that

There are three principall things mixed in euery Naturall bodie; to wit, Salte, Sulphur, and Mercurie. These are the beginnings of all Naturall things.[21]

However, it was well known that

these three principles of Chymists are not the common Salt, Sulphur, and Mercurie: but some other thing of nature, most pure and simple, which neuertheless hath some conscience and agreement with cõmon Salt, Sulphur, and Mercurie.[22]

Duchesne turned to the common Paracelsian practice of comparing mercury with spirit, sulphur with soul, and salt with body.[23] More specifically, he defined the principles in the following manner:

Mercurie is a sharpe liquor, passable, and penetrable, and a most pure & Aetheriall substantiall body: a substance ayrie, most subtill, quickning, and ful of Spirit, the foode of life, and the Essence, or terme, the next instrument.

Sulphur is that moyst, sweet, oyly, clammy, original, which giueth substance to it selfe; the nourishment of fire, or of natural heat, endued with the force of mollifying, and of gluing together.

Salt, is that dry body, saltish, meerely earththy, representing the nature of Salt, endued with wonderfull vertues of dissoluing, congealing, clensing, emptying, and with other infinite faculties, which it exerciseth in the individuals, and seperated in other bodyes, from their individuals.[24]

The "argument of the mean" is brought forth once again to prove why all three principles must be present in every material substance.

For as a man can neuer make good closing morter, of water and sand onely, without the mixture of lime, which bindeth the other two together like oile and glue: so Sulphur or the oily substance, is the mediator of Salt and Mercurie, and coupleth them both together: neither doth it onely couple them to death, but it also represse and contemperate the acrimonie of Salt, and the sharpenesse of Mercurie, which is found to bee very much therein.[25]

Since they are said to be mixed in all substances, Duchesne went on to show how they might be recognized by their properties. He suggested that enough is known of the properties of these principles to estimate roughly their proportions in the metals.[26] Even in the three elements we may discern the three principles:

For out of the element of Water, the iuyces and metallick substances do daily break forth in sight: the vapours of whose moysture or iuyse more spirituous, do set forth Mercury: the more dry exhalations, Sulphur: and their coagulated or congealed matter, Salt.[27]

In air the activity and power of the winds betray a mercurial spirit while the comets and lightning are an evidence of sulphur. Even salt may be identified in air through the thunderbolt or the "stone of the lightening". Finally, in earth "the Mercurial spirits shewe themselues in the leaues and fruites; the Sulphurus, in the flowers, seedes, and kirnels: The salts, in the wood, barke, and rootes. . . ."[28] These same principles may be found in all living creatures for the properties of sulphur may be seen in the grease, tallow, and marrow, which burn, while the salt is the bones and other hard parts, and mercury may be identified with the blood, the humours, and the vaporous substances.[29] Besides these observational tests for the three principles, Duchesne attributed to them various other qualities such as

tastes in Salt, most chiefly: odours in Sulphur: colours out of both, but most chiefely out of Mercurie: because Mercurie hath the volatile Salt of al things, ioyned unto it.[30]

The traditional four humors—blood, yellow bile, black bile, and phlegm—were summarily rejected by Duchesne and in their place he offered a totally new humoral theory. Making his humors analogous to the three principles, he limited their number to three and based them upon the three fluids most closely associated with the Galenic vascular system. Thus the first of these humours was to be the chyle, while the second, which he called the blood, corresponded closely to what we would distinguish as the venous blood.

The third of the humours, is that which after sundry reterations of the circulations, made by the much vital heate of the heart, doth very farre exceede in perfection of concoction: the other two, which may be called the elimentary or nourishing humour of life, and radical Sulphur: the which is dispearced by the arteries throughout the whole body, and is turned into the whole substance thereof.[31]

Further, he went on to suggest that as there is a continual circulation of the elements in the macrocosm,[32] so also there is a circulation of the blood in man as well. However, the circulation suggested by Duchesne does not compare with the circulation of the blood as we now understand it. Rather, it is in the sense of the circulation of a liquid in a chemical distillation.[33]

Like most Paracelsians Duchesne upheld the principle of like curing like, rather than the ancient method of seeking cures in contraries.[34] Also, although he was convinced that the purpose of chemistry was to prepare medicines, nevertheless he was not above summarizing the directions laid down by Paracelsus in the *Aurora* for the transmutation of lead to antimony.[35]

In his description of the three principles Tymme followed the Duchesne work closely, and he explained the need of them in the formation of bodies by the argument of the mean as Duchesne had done.[36] Similarly he pointed out the existence of the three principles in the heavens (fire), the air, the waters, and the earth,[37] and as Duchesne had done, he showed that these principles exist in the animate as well as the inanimate world. As his example, he chose the egg, whose yolk is sulphurous, whose white is mercurial, and whose shell is salty.[38] Again like Duchesne, he placed strong emphasis on the correspondences between the macrocosm and the microcosm. Although there is no reference in his work to the circulation of the blood, Tymme repeated the neo-Platonic view that the heart in man is comparable to the Sun in the universe.[39] And in an interesting reference to the Copernican system, Tymme rejected the heliocentric universe not necessarily because he felt that it was wrong, but rather because he felt that it is impossible to tell which of the two systems is the correct one. In such a case it is safer for the scholar to choose tradition instead of novelty.[40] The implication is clear—for Tymme the Paracelsian universe could be proven by recourse to observation, experiment, and Biblical authority, while the evidence supporting the Copernican system seemed far less convincing.

Tymme is an interesting figure and there can be no doubt that he did much to spread the knowledge of Paracelsian thought on the theory of the elements and principles. In this connection it is interesting to note that like many Paracelsians, and like Duchesne himself, Tymme seldom, if ever, mentioned Paracelsus.[41] This mystic system of thought was not ascribed to such a recent philosopher, but rather to the ancient sage Hermes in typical alchemical fashion. *The Practise of Chymicall, and Hermeticall Physicke* was the most important work of Paracelsian theory so far available from the English presses. However, there were expressed in it some considerable variations from the views of Paracelsus such as Duchesne's own theory of the humors. In essence the system of Duchesne was built around the three principles, and triads of all sorts were compared and connected with salt, sulphur, and mercury. They are analogous to body, soul, and spirit; the new three-humor theory is dependent upon them; and even the four elements are reduced to three and then assigned a passive role in relation to the active principles. In keeping with this approach, Tymme also delved into numerical mysticism and pointed to the deep significance of the number three—which not only refers to the three principles and the three elements, but also to the mysterious unity of the Holy Trinity,

ALCHYMYA.

Printed at London, by Henrie Denham.
1 5 7 6.

PLATE I. *Chemically prepared medicines were emphasized in* The
Newe Jewell of Health (1576). *The illustration from the title page of
this work pictures some of the more common equipment found in an
alchemist's laboratory in the sixteenth century.* (*Courtesy Houghton
Library, Harvard University.*)

PLATE 2. *Portrait of Robert Fludd. Frontispiece from the* Philosophia Sacra (*Frankfort, 1626*). (*Courtesy Houghton Library, Harvard University.*)

the three dimensions, the triad of beginning, middle, and end, and that of past, present, and future.[42] Although the five principles may date from *Le grand miroir* (1584), in England there was no such suggestion until much later in the seventeenth century.

The Duchesne influence may be followed by examining the works of several authors who had read the Tymme translation. The anonymous author of the *Philiatros* (1615) intended his work to serve as a reconciliation of the views of the Galenists and the Paracelsians. His compromise is a strongly biased one, however, for although he praised both sects he came out in favor of the chemists' point of view on all the crucial points on which he took any definite stand.

Comparing the different groups of physicians to the divided Christian sects, the author showed that despite their differences all Christians ultimately turn to the Bible and similarly all physicians depend upon Hippocrates. As the theologian must authenticate the books of the Bible, so too the physician must judge the authenticity of the various parts of the Hippocratic corpus.[43] One group may choose certain works while others may reject the same.

Hereupon hath followed a libertie of raising Opinions. And to speak a litle of this Art; some haue taught, that under the Moon there be 4 Elements (Fire, Ayre, Water, Earth) whereof all earthly bodyes consist. Others reiect that of Fire (supposed betweene ye Moone and the Ayre) howsoeuer meane time, they affirme that the Heauens themselues by Fire: and this doth Pliny of old seeme to teach. And of late, Scribanius in his Physickes, with Doctor Bright his conniuence upon it. The Chymists againe gainesay such Elements to be ye matter whereof the Earthly body ariseth propounding in stead thereof, Salt, Sulphur, and Mercury: And these 3 they present to the Eye, upon separation made by the art of Fire.[44]

Professing again his love for Galen and Paracelsus he went on to pay tribute to the traditional four humors, but he stated that

Now, all are called into question sauing Blood: "seeing Humors (as some define it) is a liquid Body contained in the hollownesse of the parts, as matter destinated to the nourishment of the said parts." Whereas they labour to prooue Flegme, Choler, and Melancholy to be plaine Excrements seuered from the Blood.[45]

On some of the crucial issues dividing the Galenists and the iatrochemists the author of this work showed that at heart he was a chemist. He rejected the doctrine of contraries and instead noted with approval the enunciation of the like-curing-like principle as set forth by Severinus.[46] He noted approvingly Stephen Bredwell's definition of chemistry as "the most noble instrument of Naturall knowledge",[47] and with an enthusiasm unexpected in this tract he exhorted his readers to

Put then on Gloues and Cuffes, for you must to the fire, and happily to the fiery Furnace. If fire seuer Mettals, it can more easily seuer in an Herbe, what is heterogeniall and differing in Nature. Common distillation yea, the Cookes Ordinary boylings doe manifest that. But further Art sheweth more; yea, so much, as one well saith, that the reason of man, without the light of the fornace, would neuer haue reached unto it. For heere in your Glasse Earth will be turned into water, water conuerted into ayre, and ayre into fyre. Then downe againe, fire condensed, turned into Ayre. Ayre thickned conuerting into water; and water made grosse, become Earth. And betweene euery working, many things worthy admiration. Here you shall meete with a pure Ethereall Mercury as ready to fly, as he whom the Poets fayne to trudge betweene Iupiter & Pluto. And here you find his Opposite Earth—salt, together with his Medium, or a thirde substance, by whom the sayd extremes are coupled by his Oylie nature, and this they terme Sulphur. Nor is there any Creature which in this Chymicall separation, admitteth not these three: though with wonderfull difference of Quantitie and Qualitie. Besides which there remaineth nothing sauing the Terra damnata, a meere Reiectaneum.[48]

Returning for a moment rather distastefully to his self-appointed role as arbiter between the two sects, he affirmed that of course there is no reason why all medicines should come from the furnace, but then he went on to state unequivocally that naturally the chemical medicines are more valuable since they represent purified substances.[49]

Like many other Paracelsians of this period our author too

felt called upon to mention the Copernican theory, yet on this topic he came close to maintaining his neutrality. After comparing the heliocentric universe with the geocentric universe which "almost all doe teach", he quotes an almanac-maker to the effect that the traditional view is the "Old and usual dotage", but the other is truly "Alethenticall".[50]

The author of this work, while trying to maintain his neutrality between the Galenists and the Paracelsians, had really produced one of the more inflammatory works in favor of the greater use of chemistry. In his short references to theoretical topics he uses several arguments similar to those of Duchesne. He seems to have been aware of the new humoral theory, he made mention of the fact that some wished to drop fire as an element, and he repeated the argument of the mean to explain the existence of the three principles in all substances.

Duchesne's views on the elements were to be broadcast in a far more important work, John Woodall's *The Surgions Mate* (London, 1617). D'Arcy Power considered this one of the "epoch-making books in British surgery", and in essence it is a practical guide for sea-going surgeons or surgeons' mates. As such it had a wide circulation, and enlarged editions appeared in 1639 and 1655. One of its most famed passages occurs where the author insisted that the ship's surgeon should take on oranges, limes, or lemons to combat scurvy as soon as the ship reached the Indies.[51]

As might be expected in a practical work for surgeons, the bulk of the volume is devoted to descriptions of instruments, procedures, and ointments. Woodall's Paracelsian viewpoint is clearly evident even here since he began his section of "Emplaisters . . . which are most usuall in the Surgeons chest" with a most enthusiastic account of "Emplastrum stipticum Paracelsi".[52] He also included an eight-page discussion of the use of the "Laudanum opiat Paracelsi" which he recommended enthusiastically as a narcotic. He noted that his source for this description was Oswald Croll's *Basilica Chimica*.[53]

But besides these practical prescriptions, Woodall added some theoretical material at the end of the book dealing with the elements and the principles. Here he discussed the sulphur-mercury theory of the metals which he approved of, and he described each of the Paracelsian principles in verse.[54] In typical fashion he stated that all natural things are made up of the three principles and he identified the volatile part with mercury, the fatty portion with sulphur, and the ashes remaining after combustion as salt.[55] In discussing the four elements Woodall stated that

The foure Elements are Fire, Ayre, Water, and Earth. But the diuision which the Chymists of these times pleade for touching the Elements, Iosephus Quercitanus expresseth in these words following: saith hee, the whole world is diuided into two Globes, to wit, into the superiour Heauen, which is Aetheriall and Ayrie, & into the inferiour Globe which containeth the water, and the earth. The superiour Globe which is Aetheriall, hath in it fire, lightening, and brightnesse, and this fiery Heauen is our formall and essentiall Element, the water and earth are the other two Elements: so he concludes, there is but three, and with him all the chymists of latter times subscribe, affirming that number most perfect which agreeth with the euerlasting Trinity.

Paracelsus in a treatise of his, called Meteorem, Cap. 1 mentioning the difference betwixt foure and three Elements, hath these words. Touching fire, saith he, fire which is esteemed one of the foure elements, can stand with no reason so to be: but as touching the Earth, the Water, and the Ayre, they are truly elements; for they giue element to man, but as touching fire, it giueth no element, it hath no part in the breeding of man-kinde, for it is well possible for a man to be bred, and to liue without fire; but neyther without ayre, water, nor earth can man liue, for in truth from the Heauens by helpe of the other two elements doth proceed sommer and winter, cold and heat, and all nourishment and increase whatsoeuer without the helpe of fire. Therefore are the Heauens the fourth element, yea and the first, for the sacred worde sheweth us that in the beginning God made heauen and earth, shewing that heauen was the first made, and in the outward heauens are included the water and earth, which saith Paracelsus may be compared to wine contained in a vessell, for wine is not gathered and prepared without a vessell first had and ready, prouing also manywaies that the fire is included within the Element of Ayre, & is no Element of it selfe.[56]

Thus John Woodall approved of the restriction of the elements to three, and although he managed to find authority for this doctrine in the work of Paracelsus, he correctly attributed its then current acceptance to the influence of Duchesne. In later editions of *The Surgions Mate* (1639, 1655) the section on alchemy was enlarged and Woodall also offered a short experimental manual giving directions on how one might separate the three principles from samples of animal, vegetable, and mineral matter through distillation.[57]

Paracelsism and Traditional Alchemy

If Duchesne's works on iatrochemical theory proved to be one of the major influences on Paracelsian thought in the new century, traditional alchemy was surely another. In the late sixteenth and early seventeenth centuries there was an ever-increasing interest in alchemy on the Continent. The center of this activity was the Holy Roman Empire and the court of the Emperor Rudolph II was renowned as a gathering place of astrologers, alchemists, and mystical philosophers of all descriptions. In Elizabeth's England alchemy had been far less popular. The alchemical verses of Thomas Charnock and others printed by Elias Ashmole in the *Theatrum Chemicum Britannicum* (1652) testify to the fact that there were Elizabethan adepts, but these men belonged to the secret tradition of alchemy and did not seek to publish their writings.[58] Queen Elizabeth herself had shown favor to a Continental alchemist (1565), one Alneto or Alvetanus, who left a short alchemical tract dedicated to her, but when he failed to deliver he was clapped into the Tower and the Virgin Queen henceforth looked on the followers of Hermes with suspicion. John Dee was perhaps the best-known English alchemist of the period, but he and Edward Kelley went to central Europe in the 1570s for notice to be taken of their work.[59] Although George Ripley's *Compound of Alchemy* was printed by Thomas Orwin in 1591, printed works on the subject are almost non-existent from English presses in the sixteenth and early seventeenth centuries. In truth there was some reason for this: the frauds of alchemical tricksters and the escapades of men such as Simon Forman were enough to disturb any honest searcher for the truth, while Francis Anthony's home-made potable gold got him into continual trouble with the Royal College of Physicians.

Nevertheless, the growing interest in all branches of natural philosophy is reflected in the slowly increasing number of English alchemical publications after 1610. Among these works are the *Praepositiones Tentationum* (1615) and *The Search for Causes* (1616) of Timothy Willis.[60] Here again may be seen the chemical interpretation of the Biblical story of the Creation.[61] Willis believed that the primeval chaos contained the two corporeal elements, water and earth, and that when the Spirit moved on the waters the resultant motion caused heat which in turn resulted in rarefaction.[62] This is the true explanation of the origin of air and fire. Only motion and light are mentioned in Genesis and these are never without heat. But heat is "the most proper passion or forme of that which we commonlie call Fire: Also of the upper Waters and their rarefaction, which agreeth with the Ayre of common Philosophie. . . ."[63] Willis then was inclined to accept a three-element theory of earth, water, and heat or fire, but he was undecided whether these names were proper for the elements.[64] He was only certain that in nature there was displayed a pronounced dichotomy of light (fire) and dark (earth) and that there was "a divider, or meane betweene [these] extreames".[65] As an authority for this Willis turned to the writings of Paracelsus, and he stated that this aspect of his work should be believed "as an article of your natural creed".[66] Other common concepts utilized by Willis are the macrocosm-microcosm explanation of the universe, number mysticism, and the belief that water is the mother of all things.[67] He concluded that the true meaning of the Emerald Tablet of Hermes may be found in the ladder of Angels connecting the macrocosm with the microcosm.[68]

Another interesting treatise from the early seventeenth century is the Λιθοθεωρικος (1621) of John Thornborough, Bishop of Bristol and Worcester under Elizabeth, James I, and Charles I. Writing in 1662, Thomas Fuller said that

I have heard his skill in chemistry much commended; and he presented a precious extraction to King James, reputed a great preserver of health, and prolonger of life. He conceived by such helps to have added to his vigorous vivacity, though I think a merry heart, whereof he had a great measure, was his best elixir to that purpose.[69]

Evidently this elixir was of more value to the Bishop than it was for the King, since James died at the age of fifty-nine while the bishop-alchemist was ninety when he passed on in 1641.

In passing from the iatrochemical writings of the Paracelsians to the work of Thornborough we can see that we are dealing with a different tradition. It is true that the English Paracelsians were often obscure and that they deliberately hid their secrets from the public. However, they still have an important place in the rise of modern science since they insisted on the need for experimentation and observation. Even the theory of the three principles was allied with the experimental approach because of its use as an explanatory device by practicing chemists. Traditional alchemy was far more wedded to the occult—to paradoxes, allegories, and theories deliberately obscured so that the uninitiated might not fathom their meaning. Most seventeenth-century Paracelsians wanted to be understood by their readers, but relatively few of the contemporary alchemists did.

The bulk of Thornborough's Λιθοθεωρικος deals with a hidden process for making the philosopher's stone. As the reader progresses through his three steps to this perfected substance— through Nihil, Aliquid, and Omnia—veiled hints are cautiously offered to him. As an example there is the following sentence dealing with the quintessence:

Nostra enim quinta essentia generata est virtute Solis nostri, et recipit Solis virtutem, et à Sole substantiam quasi incorruptibilem, et nobis

infundit calorem, naturam, et virtutem suam, quae quam magna sit, bene novit qui visitauit interiora terrae rectificando inveniens occultum lapidem, veram medicinam.[70]

Here the reader has pointed out to him a great secret—the first letters of the last nine words make VITRIOLUM.

This is a work on theoretical alchemy, and although Thornborough spoke of transmutations and the glories of his rare elixir, he never got down to telling how it really could be made. As a "true adept" he—like most other alchemists—complained of those philosophers who did not understand the art. Because of his interest in philosophical alchemy it is understandable that he objected to those who devoted their time to *"multiplicationibus, sublimationibus, calcinationibus, & fixationibus suis"*.[71]

Despite the traditional character of this volume, it is apparent that Bishop Thornborough was acquainted with newer trends in his field. Among other alchemical authorities he quoted Paracelsus,[72] and he stated that all things in the animal, vegetable, and mineral kingdoms consist of salt, sulphur, and mercury. He proceeded to show the analogy of these three with soul, spirit, and body, and he attributed corporeity to salt, color to sulphur, and odor to mercury.[73] He referred to the philosopher's stone as "nothing other than light" in a passage which suggests the light-dark dualism of Duchesne and Robert Fludd.[74] There is extant in manuscript form another treatise by the Bishop—a Letter on Chemistry to Lady Knowles dated 1614—which treats of transmutation once again in highly theoretical terms.[75] Thornborough also utilized the three principles here and suggested that they might be separated by distillation and extraction, but he gave no concrete examples.

The Bishop's tracts are of little use in themselves, but he seems to have gathered around him some of the other English alchemists of that age. One of them, a certain R.N.E., dedicated to him his translation of John Baptista Lambye's *A Revelation of the Secret Spirit declaring the most concealed secret of Alchymie* (1623). In this he paid tribute to the recently published Λιθοθεωρικος

and stated that the house of the Bishop was "an Apollinian re-
treat, as a living Library, a flourishing Academy, or a religious
Abbey".[76] Thornborough was not only an alchemist himself,
he was a friend of alchemists, and it was to him that Robert
Fludd was to dedicate one of his major works, the *Anatomiae
Amphitheatrum* (1623). Here Fludd called the Bishop *"amico
meo singulari, in eo ipso qui est vera mundi lux, et thesaurum
thesaurus"*.[77]

Robert Fludd and the Mosaic Philosophy (1574 —

We must turn to Robert Fludd for the English culmination
of all the occult strains of alchemical, Paracelsian, kabbalistic,
and neo-Platonic thought. As a close friend of Thornborough
he was in touch with the leading alchemical circle in England,
while his studies in Europe during his youth had thoroughly
steeped him in all the complexities of Paracelsian and neo-
Platonic mysticism. In the first half of the seventeenth century
he was one of England's best-known natural philosophers.
Certainly few other Englishmen of his day managed to draw the
attention of such a distinguished group as Kepler, Mersenne,
and Gassendi—each of whom wrote at least one work discussing,
and usually complaining of, Fludd's theories. To many Europeans
he seemed the most prominent of all English philosophers of his
day.

Born in Bearsted, Kent, in 1574, Fludd entered St. John's
College, Oxford, in 1591. It was there that he obtained his
B.A. (1597) and his M.A. (1598). Then, leaving England, he
spent six years as a student on the Continent. It was at this time
that he became interested in the complexities of the Paracelsian
approach to nature which had attracted so many Europeans,
but which at this date was relatively uncommon among
English scholars. In 1604 he returned to England where he
graduated M.B. and M.D. at Christ Church, Oxford. Residing
then in London, he sought admission to the Royal College of
Physicians early in 1606. However, due to his pronounced

Paracelsism, he failed the examination. Subsequent examinations in August, October, and December, 1607, proved equally disastrous, and after an examination on March 21, 1608, it was reported that he was considered worthy to be a candidate, but that he had conducted himself insolently and had offended everyone. Consequently he was once more rejected, and it was not until September 20, 1609, that he was admitted as a fellow of the College. In later years he was considered a highly respected member, and he served as Censor for 1618, 1627, 1633, and 1634.[78]

As a physician he was highly successful, and he was wealthy enough to maintain his own apothecary under his roof. In writing his short biography of Fludd in the middle of the century, Thomas Fuller referred to the mystical and dark language of Fludd's works, and he added "the same phrases he used to his patients; and seeing conceit is very contributive to the well working of physic, their fancy or faith natural was much advanced by his elevated expressions".[79]

In 1616 the German alchemist Michael Maier visited England, and although there is no direct evidence he contacted Fludd, it would seem likely that he did. This is all the more probable because Maier was closely connected with the new Rosicrucian movement, and in 1616 Fludd published his first book, which was a defence of the Brotherhood of the Rosy Cross against the attack of Andreas Libavius.[80] In this fairly short work he lashed out against the reliance of the schools on the ancients, and he summarized his views on the Creation and the origin of the elements. He delved into this in far greater detail in a series of folio volumes which he began to have published in the following year. These massive volumes which describe his "Mosaicall" or, as he modestly puts it, his "Fluddean" system of the world, resulted in the series of conflicts with Mersenne, Kepler, Gassendi, and others mentioned earlier. It was in these tomes that Fludd described in detail his alchemical cosmology—at the same time pausing to refute the heliocentric theory and to reinterpret much of the magnetic work of Gilbert. The first of these major works was the *Utriusque Cosmi Maioris scilicet et Minoris Metaphysica, Physica atque Technica* (Oppenheim, 1617), and for the next twenty years his works continued to pour forth from the presses.

Fludd, like most other Renaissance scientists, and certainly like all Paracelsians, had a bitter hatred of Aristotle even though Aristotelian influences are evident throughout his work. As his authority he preferred to turn to God's two books of revelation —one, His written book, the Holy Scriptures, and the other, nature, God's book of Creation. In objecting to the ancients, Fludd complained that their greatest fault was that they relied too much on "human or mundane wisdome" and therefore their work of necessity must be superseded by the "true wisdome" found in the Bible.[81] He deplored the fact that in his day the "heathnish philosophy" of the ancients was "adored" by Christians to the extent that Aristotle was worshiped "as if he were another Jesus rained down from heaven to open unto mankind the treasures of the true wisdome".[82] For Fludd, God is the cause of all things in our world. He is much more than simply the first efficient cause: rather, He is the "generall cause of all action in this world", which He accomplishes "by means of his blessed Spirit, which he sent out into the world".[83] It later becomes quite clear that the Sun is for him the temple housing this spirit.

Having thus disposed of the Aristotelian corpus as a heathenish philosophy not fit for Christians, Fludd went on to assert that we now have the Bible to lean upon, which is a much more profound source than the simple human reason on which Aristotle was dependent.[84] If one had to rely on any of the ancient Greeks one would do best to read the works of Plato, who along with Hermes had the advantage of being familiar with the books of Moses. As a result Fludd concluded that what there is of value in Aristotle's works must be ascribed to the little which was absorbed by him from his master.[85]

It is understandable then that Fludd felt that for the true meaning of our universe we must first turn to God's evidence as presented to us in the opening chapters of Genesis. Here we find a typical Paracelsian interpretation—Fludd described God's handiwork as the great "spagerick act"[86]—and he went on to explain that

> it was by the Spagericall or high Chymicall virtue of the word, and working of the Spirit, that the separation of one region from another, and the distinction of one formall virtue from another, was effected or made: of the which business the Psalmist meaneth where he saith: By the Word of the Lord the heavens were made, and by the Spirit from his mouth each virtue thereof.[87]

In this passage Fludd is only continuing in the tradition of the *Philosophy to the Athenians*, and it is a characteristic Paracelsian approach which we have already noted in the work of Duchesne and others. Basing himself on the Creation account in Genesis, Duchesne had explained that the Lord was in reality producing the three principles when He "divided waters from waters". Fludd followed the same general approach, differing from Duchesne only in granting more importance to the four elements. Referring to the same primeval dichotomy, Fludd stated that the origin of all things may be sought in the dark chaos (potential unity) from which arose the light (divine illumination or actual unity). He affirmed that there is true unity in this dichotomy since "Light was unto the eternall unity all one with darkness, though unto our weak capacities they are opposite in property".[88] Continuing, he explained that it was from the darkness or shades of the chaos through the divine light that there appeared the waters which are the passive matter of all other substances.[89]

This then is the true Mosaic philosophy, which is built upon the three primary elements of darkness, light, and the waters or the Spirit of the Lord. And it is with the aid of this divine knowledge that we may bring order even out of the confusion found in the writings of the ancients on this subject. With a careful analysis of their texts Fludd showed that when Aristotle wrote of the *prima materia*, Plato of the *hyle*, Hermes of the *umbra horrenda*, Pythagoras of the "Symbolicall unity", and Hippocrates of the deformed chaos, they were all writing in reality of the darkness or the dark abyss of Moses. Similarly by some name or another all of these philosophers knew something of the Mosaic "light" and "waters". However, in their interpretations they often varied far from the truth and it is to the works of Plato and the *Pymander* of Hermes that the true adept is urged to go for enlightenment.[90]

The ancient qualities are also dependent upon these three Fluddean elements. Like Paracelsus, Fludd disdained the pairing of qualities to give the elements, and he explained that "cold" is "an essentiall adherent unto privative rest, and the stout of-spring and Champion unto darkness". On the other hand, heat is the "inseparable Champion or assistant of Light".[91] Humidity however arises from the "intermediate actions and passions" of the other two, while dryness is nothing other than the absence of humidity.[92]

Light, darkness, and water, although the basic elements of Fludd's philosophy, nevertheless are still only primary elements. He explains that it is from the waters that all "secondary" elements arise. These secondary elements are none other than the ancient four elements. Fludd derived them from the primary waters in the following manner:

... the heavens above were made of the purer brighter and more worthy waters; and the Elementary world beneath, of the grosser darker and viler sort of waters, and that there was a midle kind of them, which participating of both extreames was termed the firmament, whose main office was to devide and seperate the water from the waters. Then out of the lower waters by the same word or spirit, were the Elements proportioned and placed, their severall regions, namely the Aire, the Seas, and the dry Land. So that wee see how the spirit of the Lord did fabrick the whole world, and every member thereof, out of this humid spirit or Aquatick nature. ...[93]

Thus the waters were separated first into a heavenly (fiery) portion and a terrene portion and the latter was in turn divided into the spheres of air, water, and earth.

> But the world is composed only of heaven and earth, and therefore it followeth that the whole world is made and existeth of the waters, and by the waters, consisting by the word of God; Now therefore since the Starrs of heaven are esteemed nothing else but the thicker portion of their Orbes, and again every creature which is below, is said to be compacted of the Elements, it must also follow that both the Starrs in the higher heaven and the compound-Creatures, beneath in the Elementary world, be they meteorologicall, or of a more perfect mixtion, namely Animal vegetable or minerall, must in respect of their materiall part or existence proceed from waters. . . .[94]

As proof of the elementary nature of water, Fludd pointed out that earth, air, fire, and water are easily transmutable, and hence simply by condensation and rarefaction of one element the others would come forth. Thus it is by successive heatings that earth may be transformed into water, water into air, and air into fire. And recalling an early experience he spoke of how he had been convinced that water is nothing but "condensed air".

> When I lived in the city of Memosia in Languedoch I once walked outside of the gates on a pleasant Summer day—and in a nearby stream (wishing to enjoy a swim and wash myself) I completely immersed my body. While doing this I held in my hands two rocks which I struck together. From this collision I heard under the water a tremendously loud noise. Certainly this could not have been heard if there were not air in the water since air is the medium of the sense of hearing.[95]

Similarly he felt obliged to demonstrate the aqueous nature of earth, suggesting that a lump of earth or a stone should be calcined, slurried in water, and then filtered through a linen cloth. The filtrate was then to be made strongly caustic with lye, and after distillation a salt would be found in the residue. He did not consider the fact that the salt might have derived originally from the stone, but rather used this as proof that all earthy matter originates from water.[96] From these and similar observations Fludd concluded that "earth is dense water, and water is dense air, while on the other hand, air is nothing else than dense and crass fire".[97] He then suggested that the observable differences between them are due to the different amounts of light present in them. One might reason that by distilling or boiling water over a fire one would be adding heat to it. Since heat and light are inseparably connected with one another, one could say that the operator is then adding light to the water, and with this assumption one would expect the water to be converted to air, and this is just what happens.[98] Hence, one could assume that there is a larger proportion of light in air than in water.

There was still the question of whether all of these elements could be considered truly elemental even in his "secondary" meaning of the word. We have seen that some of the later Paracelsians, especially those under the influence of Duchesne, tended to drop the element of fire. Although Fludd constantly used the four elements, and even went to experimental means to show their existence,[99] in his more detailed descriptions of the sublunary spheres he almost invariably used a three- rather than a four-sphere system. His reason for doing this was the same as that we have seen expressed by Duchesne and others. Relying on the properties of the qualities, Fludd postulated an inner sphere of cold (earth) and an outer sphere of heat (fire). Between these two extremes—both dry—he described a single middle sphere which is humid (water and air).[100]

Thus the Fluddean or Mosaic philosophy teaches that there are three primary elements: darkness, light, and the waters. These are the true origin of the four qualities of the ancients, since darkness and cold, and light and heat are related, and between these extremes there is a need for a humid mean. The four elements are also closely related with this system, since in the division of the waters of the firmament by the Lord in His divine alchemy, the upper waters became the heavens (fire) and the sublunary waters were split into the spheres of air, water, and earth. But because of the connection of the elements with the qualities as well as because of the similarity of water and air in distillation procedures, the spheres of these two are united and as a result the secondary elements must be earth, fire, and a humid sphere whose more subtle parts are air and whose more gross parts are water.

Fludd suggested other interesting relationships of the elements. At one point he equated the four elements and the quintessence with the five regular solids in much the same manner as Plato. This was a common concept of the period which had been referred to both by Duchesne and by Bishop Thornborough.[101] Fludd also related the four elements with the four cardinal winds, and as such they were identified with specific demons and integrated into his thought on the theory of disease.[102]

He had gone to considerable trouble to explain the Aristotelian elements in terms of the Mosaic philosophy. Naturally he was also aware of the three principles of Paracelsus, and although he applied these very seldom, he felt it necessary to account for them on the basis of his system. He stated that Paracelsus

posed three principles of all things; that is, Salt, Mercury, and Sulphur. And if we consider the matter carefully, we see that they come forth immediately from our principles. For from the center of the earth or the Darkness Salt is extracted . . .; Sulphur truly procedes from the soul and tincture of things, that is, from Light . . .; Mercury moreover partaking partly of Salt and partly of Fire is considered not ineptly to be within the Spirit [Waters].[103]

Fludd pointed out in one place that created things are composed of the Paracelsian three principles which he equated with the four elements of Aristotle,[104] and in another place he struck a definite Paracelsian note by insisting that there are as many different kinds of salt, sulphur, and mercury as there are types of substances.[105] However, he never made extensive use of the three principles other than utilizing them as an explanation of color.[106]

Throughout all of this may be seen the importance attached to the divine light. Indeed, the appearance of light in almost any form meant for Fludd some connection with divinity. For

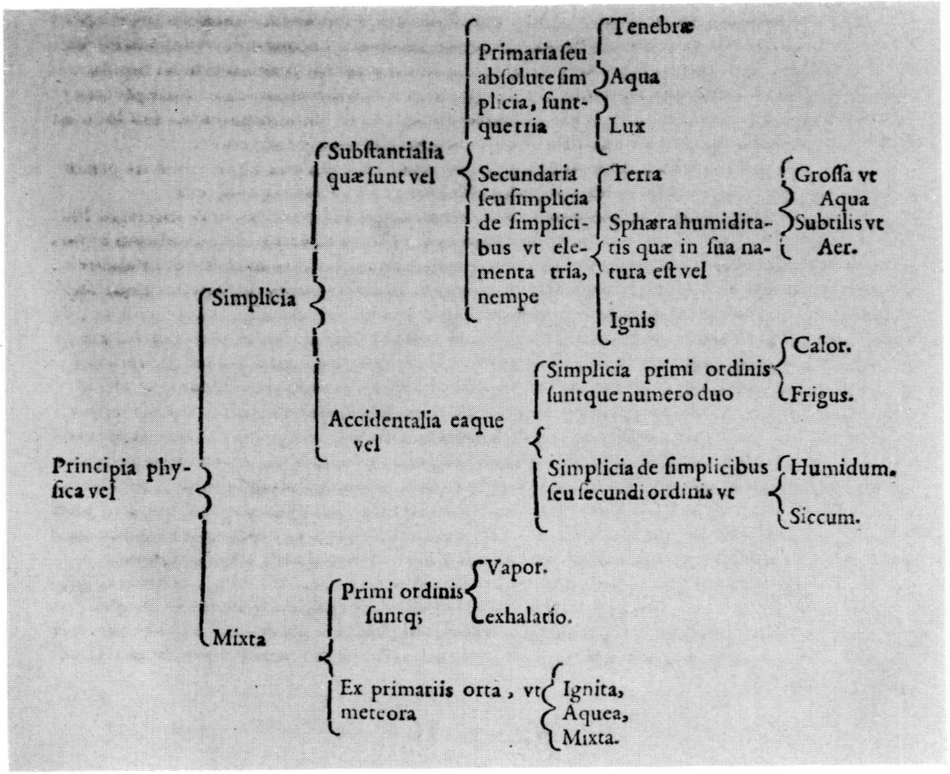

Principia physica vel

Simplicia
- Substantialia quae sunt vel
  - Primaria seu absolutè simplicia, suntque tria
    - Tenebræ
    - Aqua
    - Lux
  - Secundaria seu simplicia de simplicibus vt elementa tria, nempe
    - Terra
    - Sphæra humiditatis quæ in sua natura est vel
      - Grossa vt Aqua
      - Subtilis vt Aer.
    - Ignis
- Accidentalia eaque vel
  - Simplicia primi ordinis suntque numero duo
    - Calor.
    - Frigus.
  - Simplicia de simplicibus seu secundi ordinis vt
    - Humidum.
    - Siccum.

Mixta
- Primi ordinis suntq;
  - Vapor.
  - exhalatio.
- Ex primariis orta, vt meteora
  - Ignita,
  - Aquea,
  - Mixta.

PLATE 3. *Robert Fludd's diagrammatic scheme of the elements.* Philosophia Sacra (Frankfort, 1626), p. 6. (Courtesy Houghton Library, Harvard University.)

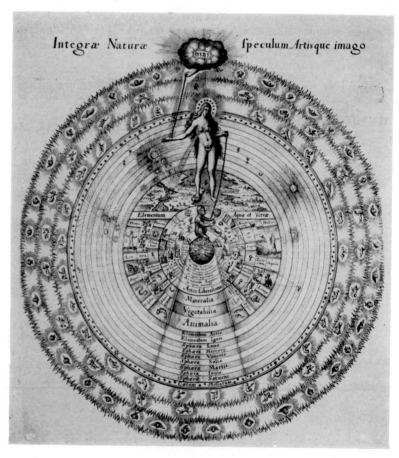

PLATE 4. *The universe of Robert Fludd as pictured in his* Utriusque Cosmi Maioris scilicet et Minoris Metaphysica, Physica atque Technica (*Oppenheim, 1617*), *pp. 4–5. The sublunary world of the elements is separated from the lower heavenly regions, and these in turn give way to the upper celestial world beyond the sphere of the stars. The power of the Creator is visualized at the top of the diagram controlling nature (here symbolized by the young woman). Nature in turn is connected with the ape, which signifies our poor reflection of divinity. (Courtesy Houghton Library, Harvard University.)*

instance, in his refutation of Aristotle's explanation of lightning, he insisted that it is a manifestation of God's will rather than something to be understood in physical terms. For proof he cited a series of cases of people who did not sufficiently cower in awe at its appearance and as a result were struck dead.[107] Fundamentally it was the light of the Lord informing the chaos which was requisite for the formation of the world. But it was this same divine light arising from the Spirit which was on the fourth day formed into the Sun and received into the aethereal heaven. Fludd was as much a proponent of the primacy of the Sun as any Renaissance neo-Platonist. He felt that its importance was shown to us above all through the Holy Scriptures—and especially in Psalm 18, 5 (Vulg) where it is written "God hath put his tabernacle in the Sun". Fludd interpreted this to mean that the Spirit of the Lord is actually in the Sun. He supported this position by theological arguments, kabbalistic analyses, and references to arithmetic, geometry, and music. Typical of his method of proof is his "astronomical" argument where he pointed to the celestial dignity of the Sun and continued:

by how much the more perfection any thing hath in it self, and excelleth the rest in glory, by so much the more it approacheth unto divinity. For as much as *Hermes* doth rightly tell us (not disagreeing in that from our Saviour Christ his doctrine) that *Bonum* and *Perfection* is onely God. Now the Macrocosmicall Sun's dignity and perfection is easily discerned, in that this Royall *Phoebus* doth sit in his chariot, even in the center or middle of the heavens, glittering with his golden hair, as the sole visible Emperour, holding the royall Scepter and government of the world, in whom all the vertue of the celestiall bodies do consist, as Jamblichus, and many other learned personages have confirmed. And *Proclus* averreth that all the powers of the stars are congregated and collected into one at the aspect of the Sun, the which are afterward disseminated by the fiery spiracle of the said Sun upon the Earth. . . .[108]

This quotation clearly betrays its neo-Platonic source and is markedly similar to the famous eulogy to the Sun of Copernicus.[109] It is also of interest to note that Fludd in support of the primacy of the Sun spoke of its centrality, meaning thereby its centrality in the heavens as opposed to the centrality of the earth in the universe as a whole. He concluded his discussion that the Sun is rightly termed "*the heart of the heaven*, because that as in the heart doth exist the lively fountain of blood which doth water and humect the other members of the body". But, he adds, we must not further conclude that the Sun is identical with God. The Scriptures attest to the fact that the Sun is created and its purpose is to house the heavenly Spirit for the benefit of the created world.[110]

Beyond its obvious significance for the macrocosm as a whole, Fludd was much concerned with the significance that the Sun has for us here on Earth as the source of light and life. Fludd considered the Sun as the purveyor of life beams required for all living creatures here on earth. These golden beams by the mercy of God are conveyed to us through the air and as such they form a necessary aethereal nutriment for all life. Fludd even interpreted the *Pater Noster* so that when we pray for our daily bread, we are actually asking for this super-celestial aerial nutriment.[111]

There is then in the air a certain super-celestial or invisible fire necessary for all life, and this, he says, was known to all true philosophers in the past (and he specifically refers to Zeno, Hermes, Zoroaster, and Heraclitus):[112]

the elementarie aire is full of the influences of life, vegetation, and of the formall seeds of multiplication, forasmuch as it is a treasure house, which aboundeth with divine beams, and heavenly gifts.[113]

He asks whether we—the microcosm—might find out anything more specific about this heavenly treasure which originates in the Sun. Of course, he replies—through the proper observation of nature. Since we know that this active celestial fire is requisite both for animal and vegetable life, Fludd examined plant life and asserted that

I can quickly demonstrate, that in the vegetable is a pure volatile salt, which is nothing but the essentiall aire of the specifick, which is wheat or bread; this volatile salt is an unctuous liquor, as white and clear as crystall; this is inwardly nevertheless full of vegetating fire, by which the species is multiplied *in infinitum*: for it is a magneticall vertue, by which it draweth and sucketh abundantly his life from the aire, and sunne beams, which is the principal treasure house of life, forasmuch as in it the eternall emanation of life did plant his tabernacle.[114]

This active and heavenly part of the air is thus in a manner fixed in living things, and through vegetable life we may examine it and show it to be a volatile salt—and this volatile salt is further identified as a volatile saltpeter. The concept of an aerial niter or a volatile saltpeter that is necessary for life is also found in the work of Duchesne (1603) and Sendivogius (1604), but both these accounts appear to derive from still earlier accounts in the Paracelsian corpus. In any case it is a concept that far antedates the famous work of John Mayow (1668, 1674).[115]

Fludd, of course, was a physician, and for him it was important to understand the role played by this aethereal saltpeter in our bodies. Like Galen, he insisted that the active part of the air was abstracted from the grosser part in the heart. And as a Paracelsian, he called this a chemical extraction.[116] But since man is a miniature copy of the great world, Fludd suggested that we might learn much by comparing our bodies with the macrocosm. Once more turning to the Sun and Psalm 18, 5, Fludd said that in man the godly tabernacle is in the heart.[117] Then relying on the fact that the earth is stationary and the Sun goes round it every day, he pointed out that the Sun, as the tabernacle of the Lord, affects the four cardinal winds which contain the breath of the Lord which is the vital nutriment that is breathed into our bodies, formed into arterial blood, and then given to the body as that spiritual nourishment without which we would all perish. Hence, the Sun travels around the earth daily in a circle and impresses on the winds as well a circular motion. This air with its circular motion is then inhaled by man, and thus the spirit of life reaches the heart and from there is carried around the body in a circular motion imitating the divine circularity.

This circular motion impressed on the blood relates not only to the spirit of the blood in the heart, but to all of the spirit of the blood in the body. He stated that as the Sun rises in the east, sets in the west, and then hastens to its original position to rise again, so also in the microcosm "does it endeavor to arise anew, and it hastens through the branches of the aorta to the South, that is, the liver, and the North or the Spleen".[118] It was in this occult fashion that Fludd proposed a system of general circulation of the spirit of the blood five years prior to Harvey.

Fludd's views on the circulation were aired in the course of his conflict with Pierre Gassendi, who rejected both Fludd's and Harvey's views on the circulation because of his belief in the existence of the pores in the septum of the heart. For Gassendi this was an overpowering argument for the seepage of the blood through the septum. Hence, a circulation was not necessary and, indeed, hardly likely. He supported his argument by stating that he had witnessed a dissection where the dissector had been able to push a probe through the septum and thus had proved the existence of these pores.[119]

Fludd in this case made his reply not with mystical arguments but rather by showing that nothing can be proved experimentally with one isolated case. He stated that he had watched many dissections performed by his friend Dr. Harvey and that in none of them could Harvey find an open passage through the septum. Hence Fludd concluded that in the dissection which Gassendi had witnessed either (1) the dissector had pushed the probe through the septum by breaking the tissue, or (2) if there were really an opening present it represented an exception to the general rule. In this instance Fludd's arguments are sound, but in general he was more interested in appealing to the Mosaic philosophy for authority.[120]

Fludd is well known for his description of the burning candle standing in water and covered by a glass bulb. The fact that the water rises as the candle burns had been known in ancient times to Philo of Byzantium, and it is probable that Fludd became aware of this phenomenon through his knowledge of the ancient sources. It would be pleasant to report that he identified the decrease in volume of the air with the consumption of a specific portion of it. One might almost expect him to have done this since, although air was a secondary element to him (or, at least,

Fludd's illustration of the candle experiment. From the *Tractatus Secundus De Naturae Simia seu Technica macrocosmi historia* (2nd edition, Frankfort, 1624), p. 471. (Courtesy Houghton Library, Harvard University.)

water–air is defined as an element in his system), he also postulated an active component referred to earlier which may be identified with the breath of the Lord, fire, or with saltpeter.[121]

If Fludd had equated this divine nitro-aerial spirit with a material component in the atmosphere his experiment with the candle could well have led to important investigations. However, he failed to grasp the real significance of this experiment even though he used it several times in his works. In the

Utriusque Cosmi Maioris scilicet et Minoris of 1617 Fludd explained that the rise of the water is proportional to the amount of included air in the flask because "air nourishes fire, and in nourishing it it is consumed, and lest there be a vacuum admitted, water, which is the third element, takes over the place of the consumed air".[122] Two years later he used the same experiment to illustrate the relationship between the soul and the body.[123] Finally, in 1631, he made use of it a third time in a refutation of the Aristotelian explanation. By this time the experiment was quite well known, for Fludd complained that the Peripatetics were employing it to show that heat attracts water. To him this was plain folly, for when one warmed the bulb of his thermoscope the heated air inside depressed the water and therefore the opposite was true. According to Fludd the water rises in the bulb not because of the attractive power of the flame (heat), but because the air becomes rarefied. Consequently with the cold (water) entering the flame is extinguished.[124] These explanations are interesting, but Fludd's purpose in the experiment was (1) to show that a vacuum was not created, (2) to show the relationship between the soul and the body, and (3) to explain the relationship of heat and water on the basis of expansion and contraction. He was not interested in the air which was consumed nor was he interested in the properties of the air before and after combustion. Hence, by not asking the proper questions he did not arrive at results which we would consider to be of any particular value today.

Fludd's fundamental dichotomy of light and darkness was stretched by its author much further than simply to account for the origin of the world, its heavenly arrangement, and its relationship to the macrocosm-microcosm. We have seen how Fludd equated the primary elements of light and darkness with heat and cold. The action of these in turn could be seen in condensation and rarefaction, and thus it is through a universal system of expansion and contraction that Fludd explained the continuing influence of God upon our world. He felt that the most important element involved in these effects was water and that its action might be studied experimentally by means of a thermoscope.[125] This instrument made visible the expansion and contraction of air confined over water with temperature changes. While this is really nothing more than a crude barometer such as that described by Galileo earlier, for Fludd it was proof that

the catholick Actor was and is the Word or Spirit of God, who acteth first in his Angelicall Organs, by the Starrs, and especially the Sun in Heaven above, and winds beneath, upon the generall sublunary Waters or Elements, according unto his volunty, altering of it after a four-fold manner, through the formall properties of the four Winds, and that either by Condensation or Subtiliation, into diverse shapes and dispositions.[126]

To this English philosopher the doctrine of expansion and contraction was a universal basis for an explanation of nature, and it was the more to be praised since it could be linked with God's will. Fludd utilized this principle time and time again as experimental evidence for his theories. For instance, he was able to obtain the three states of matter by heating and cooling water. This was for him adequate proof of the interrelation of matter and evidence that water is the mother of all elements. He used the principle also as an explanation of clouds and rain, which were nothing more than compressed air.[127]

The attraction and repulsion exhibited by the magnet give evidence also of this universal power. Fludd had studied the *De Magnete* and he refused to ignore what he felt were the errors expressed by William Gilbert in that work.

For who can believe that the earth it self, much less the particulars thereof, can have any Virtue radically from it self; when it is evident, that as well the earth as the heavens, came radically out of the waters? And therefore as the heaven was before the earth, it must needs follow, that the formall Virtue of the earth did totally descend from heaven, and consequently the earth had no such property from it self.[128]

Here he was referring to Gilbert's belief that the earth is a large magnet. A natural force similar to magnetism might be seen in the use of the dowsing rod in the search for precious metals.

Here it seemed that the hazel fork had a sympathy for the metal which acted at a distance much like magnetism. Universal sympathy, however, could derive ultimately only from divinity.[129]

In his theory of disease Fludd adopted a half-way solution to the conflict between the Galenists and the Paracelsians.[130] The ancients had explained the occurrence of disease as an upset of the four humors in the body. Paracelsus in rejecting these humors had found it necessary to picture disease as a calamity which came to man from without and which became localized in specific organs. Duchesne found both of these ideas unsatisfactory and instead drew up a new humoral theory which was closely interrelated with the three principles of Paracelsus. Fludd, however, took no notice of the Duchesne innovation and instead took over into the Fluddean philosophy both the ancient humors and the ontological viewpoint of Paracelsus. Pagel has shown that Fludd maintained the ancient humoral theory in a close connection with astrological influences on the body. However, at the same time

he maintains that the cause of disease represents the essence of disease, and taking into consideration both the ancient belief in the influence of harmful exhalations (Galen) and the emphasis laid by Paracelsus on the importance of an aerial chaos of the finest corporality, he decides that the causes of disease must be the winds.[131]

There exist in the atmosphere "spiritus mali" which may enter the body through inhalation or the pores of the skin. These substances are under the control of four demons which are identified with the four elements, and man may be pictured as being protected by four angels who help ward off these seeds of bodily destruction. Hence this essentially "modern" concept of disease is coupled with Fludd's usual mystic correspondences.[132]

In view of his interest in alchemy one might expect that Robert Fludd would have been one of the primary spokesmen in England for chemically prepared medicines. He did recognize this as one of the important aspects of this universal science, but he devoted little space to this topic in his printed works. One of the few aspects of practical therapy he considered in any detail was the use of the "Weapon Salve". His interest was drawn to this because of its connection with the universal power of sympathy, and he was perhaps driven to write fully of it because of the controversy he became involved in concerning it. In the seventeenth century this cure was widely thought to have been a Paracelsian innovation and it was attributed to him by such well-known authors as Porta and Croll. In essence the cure amounted to the following: after a person was wounded the wound itself was simply cleaned daily with white wine or urine and wrapped with a clean linen cloth. The weapon, however, was dipped in the patient's blood or anointed in some complex concoction in which human blood was the main ingredient. "The cure is done by the magnetique attractive power of this Salve, caused by the Starres, which by the mediation of the ayre, is carried and adjoyned to the Wound, that so the Spirituall operation thereof may bee effected."[133] Other details of this do not concern us here. The point is that Fludd approved of this cure primarily because of its relation to the doctrine of sympathy and antipathy and it seemed to be further proof of the intimate connection between the macrocosm and the microcosm.

He appears to have been shocked then to find himself bitterly attacked and accused of being a magician because of his belief in the Weapon Salve. His antagonist in this debate was a little-known English clergyman, William Foster, who, after recounting the reputed wonders of the Weapon Salve, stated flatly that such feats could only be compared with witchcraft. But, he continued,

The Author of this Salve, was Philippus Aureolus, Bombastus Theophrastus Paracelsus. Feare not Reader, I am not conjuring, they are onely the names of a Conjurer, the first inventer of this Magicall oyntment. . . . For mine owne part, to satisfie my selfe and my Readers, I will goe no farther than to the Tract wherein the Vnguent is described, and there to the prescription next adjoyned, which is a Receipt to cure one decayed in Nature, unable to perform due benevolence. . . . Take an horse-shooe cast from a horse, let it be wrought into a trident Forke, impresse these and these Characters on it, put a staffe of such a length into the socket for the stale of it; let the Patient take this Forke and sticke it in the bottome of a River of such a depth, and let it remaine sticking there so long as is prescribed, and he shal be restored to his former manlike abilitie. If this be not Witchcraft, I know not what is! Now then Paracelsus being a Witch, and this experiment being placed amongst his Diabolicall and magicall conclusions, it cannot choose but be Witchcraft, and come from the grand master of Witches, the Diuell, if Paracelsus were (as most repute him) the Author and Founder of it.[134]

Having thus established his major point, Foster went on to accuse the following authors of promoting this devilish cure: Paracelsus, Croll, Porta, Cardan, Burgravius, Goclenius, van Helmont (probably one of the earliest references to him in England), Fludd, and even Sir Francis Bacon.[135] In spite of his attack on all of these, he saved his most bitter words for Fludd and he suggested that Fludd's defence of the Salve is enough to make him suspected of witchcraft. To Foster his reputation was so shady that it was a wonder "that King Iames (of blessed memory) should suffer such a man to live and write in his Kingdome".[136] Foster suggested that such wounds that appear to be cured by this method actually are cured by the simple means of keeping them constantly clean.[137]

Fludd replied immediately in a work which pointed out Foster's lack of knowledge to deal with such problems which should be left to "learned Physicians" rather than "Schoolemen, who deale onely in imaginary speculative Philosophy".[138] Also there was no need to call him a magician since even his Continental opponent Pierre Gassendi had defended him from this charge.[139] Indeed, this cure as well as all other cures should be considered as gifts of God, not as tools of the Devil.[140] Compared to Foster's fanatical abuse, Fludd's reply was relatively dignified.

The most interesting part of this whole affair is the attitude toward Paracelsus expressed by the two men. Foster's attack was certainly the most vigorous one yet made on him in England, and while allusions to the magic of Paracelsus had been voiced in England earlier than this, there had been no such frontal accusation of witchcraft. Here was Fludd's great opportunity to uphold the work of his predecessor. However, instead of doing this, he took the attitude—with some justification—that Foster's work was nothing more than an attack on him and his system. His only mention of Paracelsus in his reply was to praise him along with all the other men Foster had condemned.[141] This was in keeping with Fludd's general attitude, for like many Paracelsians he was both proud of his own originality and certain of the antiquity of the "true medicine". As a result, references by Fludd to Paracelsus are very uncommon.[142]

Fludd was perhaps the best-known English scientist of his generation on the Continent. But his science was far removed from that of his contemporary, Galileo. For him, true alchemy was the key to the understanding of the universe, and although he believed in practical alchemy,[143] he was not particularly interested in that side of the science. Rather he sought for divine musical harmonies and mathematical interrelationships of the macrocosm and the microcosm. This was the alchemical world picture to which his Continental adversaries objected. Pierre Gassendi, noting Fludd's rejection of the Copernican system, despairingly commented that "he understands another non-volatile Earth, and another central Sun, than that commonly understood by us".[144] Kepler, of course, challenged Fludd's whole scheme of the divine harmony. For Kepler, Fludd's application of music to the study of the heavens was certainly not improper—it was only that Fludd's whole approach and calculations were wrong while his own explanation of the celestial harmonies based on calculations obtained from observational data was correct. Kepler proudly compared his own mathematical approach to astronomy with the occult, chemical, Hermetic, and Paracelsian works of Fludd.[145] Be that as it may, today some of the speculations of Kepler seem not far removed from those of Fludd.

In England Fludd's stress on the importance of the divine light in the formation of the world was questioned by Patrick Scot in his *Tillage of Light* (1623), and even Francis Bacon complained of those who tried to explain all nature in terms of light "as if it were a thing half way between things divine and things natural".[146] Mersenne, in his commentary on Genesis (1623), specifically attacked him for his comparison of the Creation with a divine chemical separation, and he objected as well to the sum total of alchemical occultism in his *La Vérité des Sciences* (1625). When Fludd replied in his *Sophia Cum Moria Certamen* (1629) and his *Summum Bonum* (1629) it would seem that he completely misunderstood Mersenne's argument. Mersenne had complained of the alchemical interpretation of Scripture and the occult language of the alchemists as well as their mystical explanation of natural events. Fludd, however, felt that Mersenne was only confusing the search for gold with true alchemy.[147] And yet Fludd's inability to understand Mersenne's viewpoint was coupled with frequent appeals to mechanical analogies, fresh observations of nature, and a truly scientific ability to point out the methodological weaknesses in Gassendi's work on the permeability of the septum. Unfortunately he depended upon experimental evidence far too seldom.

In evaluating Fludd's universe it is necessary to remember that he was neither a scientist in the modern sense nor an astronomer. Rather, he was a physician steeped in the Paracelsian, Hermetic, and neo-Platonic sources, who felt that for a true interpretation of the universe the scholar should turn to mystical alchemy, which for him was the same as true theology. Because of this, one would hardly expect from him a mathematical description of the heavens. This would have been beyond his ability and of little interest to him. For Fludd the highest form of mathematics was the understanding of the properties and relationships of numbers in the Pythagorean tradition. For his strongest arguments Fludd, whenever possible, turned to the Holy Scriptures, which he considered irrefutable. It was characteristic of the man that he was completely unable to understand how Gassendi could write that it was not the intention of the Scriptures to teach us physics.[148] Thus we find Fludd fundamentally separated from his "Galilean" contemporaries by his insistence on the Bible as the ultimate source of physical knowledge.

On the other hand, the strong neo-Platonic and Paracelsian influences evident in the Mosaic philosophy are common in many aspects of Renaissance science. Fludd's attack on the ancients, and the close relationship of science and religion on which he insisted, were typically Paracelsian. The alchemical description of the Creation was a basic concept in the work of Paracelsus, and it had also been spelled out in detail by Duchesne, whom Fludd would seem to have read with care. The Paracelsian reduction of the four elements to three was also gaining currency in the early seventeenth century, primarily because of the popularity of Duchesne's work. But Fludd's emphasis on three of the traditional elements when compared with Duchesne's emphasis on the three principles brings out one difference between the two men: Duchesne was far more concerned with the practical application of chemistry to medicine than Fludd. Indeed, Fludd was much less interested in experimental work than most other iatrochemists, although there is no question that he could argue from experimental observations when he so desired.

Yet in spite of the works of Robert Fludd, Thomas Tymme, and others discussed in this chapter, Paracelsian thought was uncommon among Englishmen in the first forty years of the seventeenth century. For like the earlier published tracts, these works never attained great popularity and they were for the most part all limited to single editions. The work of John Woodall is an exception to this rule since it was revised and enlarged for two later editions. But the Paracelsian theory which was available in Woodall's *Surgions Mate* was offered only in the form of an appendix to this popular surgical treatise. As for Fludd's multi-volume tomes, they attained popularity only on the Continent and most of them were printed there. Only his answer to Foster and the second edition of the *Mosaicall Philosophy* were printed in England, and the latter only appeared in 1659, many years after his death, at a time when there was a revival of occult thought in England. During his lifetime Fludd had to complain of the lack of interest of his countrymen in his mystical researches into nature. He compared the splendid reception given to his works in Germany with the stinging attack on him by the unknown Parson Foster. Since Mersenne had accused Fludd of magic, Foster assumed that this was "one cause why he hath printed his bookes beyond the Seas. Our Universities, and our Reverend Bishops (God bee thanked) are more cautelous than to allow the Printing of Magical books here".[149] Fludd denied this accusation; he had his works printed in Germany

because our home-borne Printers demanded of me five hundred pounds to Print the first Volume, and to find the cuts in copper; but beyond the Seas it was printed at no cost of mine, and that as I would wish: And I had 16 coppies sent me over with 40 pounds in Gold, as an unexpected gratuitie for it.[150]

The same impression may be obtained by looking at some short biographies of Fludd. In 1630 J. J. Boissard published the second volume of his *Bibliotheca sive Thesaurus Virtutis et Gloriae* at Frankfort in which he claimed that the writings of Fludd would immortalize the English physician.[151] Even those scholars such as Kepler, Mersenne, and Gassendi who disagreed with him felt that Fludd's views had to be studied in detail and carefully answered. In England, however, his works were for the most part ignored, and Thomas Fuller wrote that

His works are for the English to slight or admire, for French and foreigners to understand and use; not that I account them more judicious than our own countrymen, but more inquiring into such difficulties. The truth is, here at home his books are beheld not so good as crystal, which (some say) are prized as precious pearls beyond the seas.[152]

It would appear then that the "Elizabethan compromise" was maintained throughout the first forty years of the new century. Paracelsian theory by way of the writings of Paracelsus himself had been rejected in the closing years of the sixteenth century.[153] Attempts to revive interest in this mystic cosmology through the works of the French Paracelsian Duchesne were not especially successful although we have shown that some aspects of his thought may be traced through the work of Tymme, Woodall, and Fludd. It is significant that the first half of the seventeenth century saw no foundation of an English school of Paracelsism. The interest that was shown depended to a large extent on the importation of Duchesne's theories while Fludd's complex system attracted practically no one in his own country. Both Duchesne and Fludd considered themselves to be independent authorities, and their works make little mention of Paracelsus even though they may be considered as Paracelsian in type. It is probable, then, that the lack of interest in Paracelsus and his theories is to be ascribed primarily to a basic dislike by Englishmen at this time of the mystical approach to science, whether or not the system itself was actually called Paracelsian. But if the Elizabethans had rejected the occultism of Paracelsian thought, they had accepted the usefulness of the new remedies. Their Jacobean followers approved of the first decision, and were also to find themselves in favor of the chemically prepared medicines.

Notes for Chapter Three

1. A. F. Pollard, "Thomas Tymme", *Dictionary of National Biography* (hereafter cited as *DNB*), *19* (1949–50), 1349–50.
2. Joseph Duchesne (1544–1609) was a famed sixteenth-century French Protestant physician. He had obtained his M.D. degree at Basel in 1573 but he did not return to Paris until 1593 when he became a physician to Henry IV. His fight for the acceptance of chemically prepared medicines will be related in the next

chapter. See *Larousse Dictionnaire du XIXᵉ Siècle* (Paris, 1875), *13*, 519, and Ferd. Hoefer, *Histoire de la Chimie* (2 vols., Paris, 1842–43), *2*, 27–28. Duchesne had been one of John Hester's favorite authors to translate. Prior to *The Practise of Chymicall, and Hermeticall Physicke* there had appeared in English the following works by Duchesne: *The sclopotarie of I. Quercetanus, or his booke containing the cure of wounds receiued by shot of gunne*, tr. John Hester (London, 1590). *A Breefe Aunswere of Josephus Quercetanus . . . to the exposition of Iacobus Aubertus Vindonis, concerning the original and causes of Mettalles. Set foorth against Chimistes. . . . Another exquisite and plaine Treatise of the same Josephus, concerning the Spagericall preparations and use of minerall, animall, and vegitable Medicines*, tr. and expanded by John Hester (London, 1591). The work dealing with the origin of metals sets forth a fair amount of theory and as such it is unusual among translations by Hester. However, none of these works gave the broad picture of Paracelsian thought concerning the Creation and the origin of the elements that the Tymme translation offered to the English reader.

3. The above quotations are all taken from Tymme's dedication to Sir Charles Blunt in Joseph Duchesne, *The Practise of Chymicall, and Hermeticall Physicke, for the preseruation of Health*, tr. Thomas Tymme, Minister (London, 1605), sig. A3–A4.

4. Thomas Tymme, *A Dialogue Philosophicall* (London, 1612). From the dedication to Sir Edward Coke, Lord Chief Justice of the Court of Common Pleas, sig. A3.

5. *Ibid.*

6. R. Hooykaas, "Die Elementenlehre der Iatrochemiker", *Janus*, 41 (1937), 26–28.

7. Joseph Duchesne, *Le Grand Miroir du Monde* (Paris, 1595), 169. At the opening of the book summarizing his arguments on the elements, Duchesne states that: La Nature a pour matiere les quatre elemẽs descrits auec leur accord, leur mouement, & leur nombre: dont naist une longue dispute où sont proposee diuerses opinions: pour resolution desquelles est mise en auant la sentence de Moyse qui n'establit que deux elemens productifs, l'eau & la terre, à qui Dieu donna la lumiere, comme pour forme: les admirables effects de laquelle ne sont oubliez. Pour esclarcissement de ceste sentence de Moyse, scauoir est que de toutes choses on ne peut extraire que deux elemens, l'humide & le sec, le Poete rameine le lecteur à l'experience qui s'en peut faire, & monstre qu'en toutes choses se trouuent trois principes qu'il appelle mercure, soulfre & sel, qui se rapportent aux deux elemens par luy mentionnez. Appliquant cela à l'air, à l'eau, à la terre, il prouue que l'air n'est autre chose qu'une eau rarefiee, estant, froid & humide comme elle; que la terre n'est pas froide, mais chaude: surquóy il traite de la proprieté de ces qualitez, de chaleur, & de froideur, en mõstre l'origine, & descouure les effects & differences des trois principes qu'il a mis en auant.

8. *Ibid.*, 67.

9. *Ibid.*, 177.

10. *Ibid.*, 150.

11. Duchesne, *Practise*, sig. H1 (r).
12. *Ibid.*, sig. G3 (r).
13. Francis M. Cornford, *Plato's Cosmology* (New York, 1957), 43 ff.
14. Myrtle Marguerite Cass has written that "Cardan maintains that there are only three [elements]: earth, air, and water. Fire is not an element, for it requires food, moves about, is of very fine substance, and nothing is produced from it." Girolamo Cardano, *The First Book of Jerome Cardan's De Subtilitate*, Latin text, commentary, and translation by Myrtle Marguerite Cass (Williamsport, Pa., 1934), 15. See also Jerome Cardan, *De Subtilitate* (Nuremberg, 1550), 23–24 where he states that "Sed certé sub coelo Lunae nullus est ignis. . . . Natura semper extrema mediis jungit. . . . Nam inter duo extrema non duo, sed tantum unum solet assignari medium. Quõd si statuatur, non quatuor sed tria tantum erunt elemeña.", and his *De Varietate Libri XVII* (Basel, 1557), 21, Chapter 2: "Esse aũt tria, perspicuum est: terram solidissimam, aeram tenuissimum, aquam inter haec mediam." For the attitude of Paracelsus in regard to the true elementarity of fire see below p. 100.
15. Tymme, *Dialogue Philosophicall*, 31.
16. Duchesne, *Practise*, sigs. G3–G4.
17. Tymme, *Dialogue Philosophicall*, 31.
18. Duchesne, *Practise*, sig. T4 (r).
19. Tymme, *Dialogue Philosophicall*, 31.
20. *Ibid.*, 32.
21. Duchesne, *Practise*, sig. B3.
22. *Ibid.*, sig. H3 (v).
23. *Ibid.*, sig. C4 (v), P4 (v).
24. *Ibid.*, sig. D1 (v).
25. *Ibid.*, sig. T4 (v).
26. *Ibid.*, sigs. H3–H4. He also observed that since the three principles remain in a substance no matter how it is acted on or changed, in the same way copper or iron must remain in vitriol even though their outward form has been changed.
27. *Ibid.*, sig. H2 (v).
28. *Ibid.*, sig. I3 (v).
29. *Ibid.*, sig. K2 (r).
30. *Ibid.*, sig. T3 (v).
31. *Ibid.*, sig. L1 (r).
32. *Ibid.*, sig. C4 (r).
33. This concept of the circulation of the blood as a chemical distillation has been discussed in some detail in regard to the work of Cesalpino by Pagel in his "Harvey and the Purpose of the Circulation", *Isis*, *42* (1951), 25–26. For further details on this problem and the relation of Duchesne and Fludd see below in this chapter and also in A. G. Debus, "Robert Fludd and the Circulation of the Blood", *J. Hist. Med.*, *16* (1961), 374–93. In brief, with the exception of a reference which suggests that all of the blood circulates in the body as in a chemical pelican, Duchesne discusses in detail only the venous system. He states that the blood which is carried to the heart by the vena cava

is there circulated and distilled over in a purer form to the brain where it is redistilled or circulated a second time. In the Tymme translation Duchesne states that:

> ... the same blood being carried into the heart, by the veyne called Vena Caua, which is as it were the Pellican of nature, or the vessel circulatory, is yet more subtilly concocted, and obtaineth the forces as it were of quintessence, or of a Sulphurus burning Aquavita, which is the original of natural & unnatural heat. The same Aquavita being carried from hence by the arteries into the Balneum Maris of the Braine, is there exalted againe, in a wonderful maner by circulations; and is there changed into a spirit truly ethereal and heauenly, from whence the animal spirit proceedeth, the chiefe instrument of the soule . . . (Duchesne, *Practise*, sig. K4 (v)).

34. *Ibid.*, sig. N4 (r).
35. *Ibid.*, sig. I1 (v).
36. Tymme, *Dialogue Philosophicall*, 32.
37. *Ibid.*, 33–35.
38. *Ibid.*, 36.
39. *Ibid.*, 37.
40. *Ibid.*, 58 ff. Francis R. Johnson has discussed this notice of the Copernican system in his *Astronomical Thought in Renaissance England* (Baltimore, 1937), 261–63.
41. Duchesne, for instance, wrote that he did not always agree with Paracelsus, but he recognized that he had taught many things "almost divinely in Phisicke". Quercetanus, *Breefe Aunswere*, tr. J. Hester (London, 1591), fol. 1.
42. Tymme, *Dialogue*, 38.
43. Anon., *Philatros* (London, 1615), sig. A2.
44. *Ibid.* Another early reference to the discarding of fire as a true element may be seen in John Donne's *The First Anniversary* (1610–11) where he wrote:
    And new Philosophy calls all in doubt
    The Element of fire is quite put out.
    See Charles M. Coffin, *John Donne and the New Philosophy* (New York, 1937), 166–67.
45. *Philiatros*, sig. A2. Another early reference to the new views on the humours may be found in Thomas Walkington's *The Optick Glasse of Humors* (London, 1607) where the conservative author wrote that:
    > I know the Paracelsian will utterly condemne my endeavor for bringing the foure Humours on the stage again, they hauing hist them off so long ago, & the rather because I once treat not of their three minerals—Sal, Sulphur, and Mercurius, the Tria omnia of their quicksilver wits, which they say haue chiefe dominion in the body, (it consisting of them) and are the causes of each disease, and cure all againe by their Arcana extracted out of them: but I waigh it not, since the tongue of an adversary cannot detract from verity (sig. A3).

    Walkington (d. 1621) obtained his B.A. (1596–97) and M.A. (1600) from Cambridge. He then went on to take a B.D. at Oxford (1611) and a D.D. at

Cambridge (1613). He held various vicarages in Lincolnshire and Middlesex and his *Optick Glasse* is considered a forerunner of Burton's *Anatomy of Melancholy*. On his life see the biography by Sidney Lee in the *DNB, 20,* 548.

46. *Philiatros*, fol. 5.
47. *Ibid.*, fol. 13.
48. *Ibid.*, fol. 14.
49. *Ibid.*, fol. 14.
50. *Ibid.*, fols. A2, 2.
51. D'Arcy Power, "Epoch Making Books in British Surgery. V. The Surgeons Mate by John Woodall", *Brit. J. Surgery, 16* (1928), 4. Additional points on Woodall's life and his views on alchemy and Paracelsian thought are brought forth in A. G. Debus, "John Woodall, Paracelsian Surgeon", *Ambix, 10* (1962), 108–18.
52. John Woodall, *The Surgions Mate* (London, 1617), 40.
53. *Ibid.*, 224–32.
54. *Ibid.*, 293–306.
55. *Ibid.*, 306.
56. *Ibid.*, 309 f.
57. *Ibid.* (3rd ed., 1655), 233–46.
58. An interesting relation of the secret tradition in English alchemy and the "adoption" of Elias Ashmole by William Backhouse will be found in C. H. Josten, "William Backhouse of Swallowfield", *Ambix, 4* (1949), 1–33. On Charnock see F. S. Taylor, "Thomas Charnock", *Ambix, 2* (1946), 148–76.
59. Dee did receive recognition from the court for his work in astrology, astronomy, and mathematics. However, his alchemical work seems to have been for the most part ignored in England. The Alvetanus work, titled *Epistola de conficiendo divino Elixire sive Lapide Philosophico*, is dated 1565 and was printed in volumes 5 and 6 of Zetzner's *Theatrum Chemicum* (6 vols., Argentorati, 1659–61).
60. Timothy Willis, *Praepositiones Tentationum* (London, 1615). *The Search for Causes Containing A Theophysicall Investigation of the Possibilitie of Transmutatorie Alchemie* (London, 1616). Timothy Willis was the son of Richard Willis, a leather merchant of London. He entered the Merchant Taylors' School on April 22, 1575, and obtained a fellowship at St. John's College, Oxford, in 1578. He matriculated there in 1581, but was shortly thereafter ejected from his fellowship for certain unspecified misdemeanors. After obtaining his B.A. in 1582, he was readmitted to St. John's with the Queen's favor and later Elizabeth sent him on an embassy to Muscovy. On his life see Miss Bertha Porter, "Timothy Willis", *DNB, 62* (1900), 26.
61. *Search for Causes*, 8–11.
62. *Ibid.*, 10.
63. *Ibid.*, 11–12.
64. *Ibid.*, 12.
65. *Ibid.*, 13.

66. *Ibid.*, 49.
67. *Ibid.*, 14, 20, 33–34.
68. *Ibid.*, 86.
69. Thomas Fuller, *The Worthies of England*, ed. John Freeman (London, 1952), 615.
70. John Thornborough, Λιθοθεωρικος (Oxford, 1621), 128.
71. *Ibid.*, 31.
72. *Ibid.*, 2.
73. *Ibid.*, non-paginated "Ad Lectorem benevolum".
74. *Ibid.*, fol. 3, from the dedication to the Duke of Lennox.
75. John Thornborough, Bp. of Bristol, "Letter of Chemistry to the right Ho[ble] the Lady Knowles—dated 1614", British Museum Sloane Ms 1799 fols. 74–104.
76. John Baptista Lambye, *A Revelation of the Secret Spirit Declaring the Most concealed secret of Alchymie*, tr. R.N.E., gentleman (London, 1623), sig. A4f. The British Museum copy has written in longhand opposite the title page: "The translator (see the Epistle Dedicatory) was evidently a native of Scotland. His initials R.N.E. might stand for Robert Napier, Esq. (or of Edinburgh) a younger son of Napier of Murchiston."
77. Robert Fludd, *Anatomiae Amphitheatrum effigie triplici more et conditione varia* (Frankfort, 1623), sig. A3. In his *Mosaicall Philosophy* (London, 1659), 118, he mentions that he once resided with Thornborough at Hartlebury Castle.
78. On Fludd's life see J. B. Craven, *Doctor Robert Fludd* (Kirkwall, 1902); C. H. Josten, "Truth's Golden Harrow. An unpublished alchemical Treatise of Robert Fludd in the Bodleian Library", *Ambix*, 3 (1949), 91–150.
79. Fuller, *op. cit.*, 281.
80. Robert Fludd, *Apologia Compendiaria Fraternitatem de Roseâ Cruce Suspicionis et Infamiae Maculis Aspersam, Veritatis quasi Fluctibus abluens et abstergens* (Leiden, 1616). See also Fludd, *Tractatus Apologeticus Integritatem Societatis De Rosea Cruce defendens* (Lugduni Batavorum, 1617).
81. Fludd, *Mosaicall Philosophy*, 12–13.
82. *Ibid.*, 28.
83. *Ibid.*, 29.
84. *Ibid.*, 32.
85. *Ibid.*, 32, 42.
86. *Ibid.*, 147–48.
87. *Ibid.*, 175.
88. On the light-dark dualism, see especially Robert Fludd, *Utriusque Cosmi Maioris scilicet et Minoris Metaphysica, Physica atque Technica* (Oppenheim, 1617), 205–06. For the specific quotation referred to here see the *Mosaicall Philosophy*, 82. For Fludd on the *prima materia* see Walter Pagel, "Paracelsus and the Neoplatonic and Gnostic Tradition", *Ambix*, 8 (1960), 125–66, especially 146–47.
89. *Mosaicall Philosophy*, 82. See also, Robert Fludd, *Tomus Secundus de Super-naturali, Naturali, Praeternaturali et Contranaturali Microcosmi historia, in Tractatus*

tres distributa (Oppenheim, 1619), Chapter 9, 200–03. This chapter is titled "De principiis nostris Microcosmi, & quomodò tam cum principiis divinarum literarum, quàm cum intentionibus omnium Philosophorum & Chymicorum conveniant?"

90. *Mosaicall Philosophy*, 41–42.
91. *Ibid.*, 82.
92. *de Supernaturali*, 200–03.
93. *Mosaicall Philosophy*, 47–48.
94. *Ibid.*, 48.
95. Robert Fludd, *Clavis Philosophiae et Alchymiae Fluddanae* (Frankfort, 1633), 35.
96. Robert Fludd, *Tom. Sec. Tract. Sec. De Praeternaturali Utriusque Mundi Historia in Sectiones tres divisa* (Frankfort, 1621), 95.
97. Robert Fludd, *Anatomiae Amphitheatrum*, 25. For a similar treatment see also Fludd, *Mosaicall Philosophy*, 69–70; *Medicina Catholica seu Mysticum Artis Medicandi Sacrarium In Tomos divisum duos, 1* (Frankfort, 1629), 107; *Tom. Sec. Tract. Sec. De Praeternaturali Utriusque Mundi Historia In Sectiones tres divisa* (Frankfort, 1621), 111.
98. *De Supernaturali*, 200–03.
99. *Utriusque Cosmi* (1617), 71. Here Fludd treats a sample of wine to a series of extractions and distillations and arrives finally at a sample with five layers or regions which he says correspond to the four elements and the quintessence.
100. *De Supernaturali*, 200–03; *Medicina Catholica*, 107.
101. *Anat. Amph.*, 322–24.
102. See below and also *Med. Cath.*, 83; Pagel, "Religious Motives in the Medical Biology of the 17th Century", *Bull. Hist. Med.*, 3 (1935), 271. Note also that the elements and the demons were connected earlier by Duchesne, see above p. 90.
103. *De Supernaturali*, 203.
104. *De Praeternaturali*, 96.
105. *Med. Cath.*, 153.
106. *Ibid.*, 147–55.
107. *Mosaicall Philosophy*, 115–19.
108. See Fludd's series of eight arguments in *ibid.*, 61–64.
109. Compare this quotation from Fludd with the famous quotation from Copernicus:

> In the middle of all sits the Sun enthroned. In this most beautiful temple could we place this luminary in any better position from which he can illuminate the whole at once? He is rightly called the Lamp, the Mind, the Ruler of the Universe; Hermes Trismegistus names him the visible God, Sophocles' Electra calls him the All-seeing. So the Sun sits as upon a royal throne ruling his children the planets which circle round him.

(Thomas S. Kuhn, *The Copernican Revolution* (Cambridge, Mass., 1957), 130.) The concept of the Sun's centrality in the heavens was common among Renaissance neo-Platonists. For a more detailed discussion of Fludd's views on this subject see A. G. Debus, "The Sun in the Universe of Robert Fludd".

110. *Mosaicall Philosophy*, 65.
111. *Ibid.*, 162.
112. *Ibid.*
113. *Ibid.*, 163.
114. *Ibid.*
115. For a more complete discussion of this problem see the present author's "The Aerial Niter in the Sixteenth and Early Seventeenth Centuries", *Actes du Dixième Congrès International d'Histoire des Sciences* (2 vols., Paris, 1964), 2, 835–39; "The Paracelsian Aerial Niter", *Isis*, 55 (1964), 43–61. Other studies of this tradition in relation to John Mayow include the following: Henry Guerlac, "John Mayow and the Aerial Nitre—Studies on the Chemistry of John Mayow, I", *Actes du Septième Congrès International d'Histoire des Sciences* (Jerusalem, août, 1953), 332–49; Henry Guerlac, "The Poets' Nitre—Studies in the Chemistry of John Nayow, II", *Isis*, 45 (1954), 243–55; J. R. Partington, "The Life and Work of John Mayow (1641–1679)", *Isis*, 47 (1956), 217–30, 405–17. Partington has shown that there were references to an active nitrous part of the air prior to Mayow, and Guerlac has traced this tradition back to Sendivogius in the early years of the seventeenth century. Pagel more recently has shown that the concept of a vital nitrous part of the air is Paracelsian in origin (Pagel, *Paracelsus*, 118, footnote 324).
116. *Mosaicall Philosophy*, 164–65.
117. The present author has discussed Fludd's views on the circulation in more detail in his "Robert Fludd and the Circulation of the Blood", *J. Hist. Med.*, 16 (1961), 374–93. It is interesting to recall (see note 33, this chapter) that Duchesne had suggested a series of circulations of the blood in the liver, the heart, and the brain which might be likened unto a connected series of chemical distillations. Fludd borrowed this system from Duchesne in its entirety with its implication of "local" circulations. The mystical general circulation of the blood described above is a second sense of the word circulation used by Fludd.
118. Fludd, *Anatomiae*, 266.
119. Pierre Gassendi, *Epistolica exercitatio in qua principia philosophiae Roberti Fluddi, medici reteguntur, et ad recentes illius libras adversus R.P.F. Marinum Mersennum . . . respondetur* (Paris, 1630), 133–36.
120. Fludd, *Clavis*, 33–34.
121. See *De Supernaturali*, 203, or even more specifically the *Clavis Philosophiae*, 33. For Fludd this spirit of the Lord or the nitro-aerial part of the air is the active part of the air and is inhaled into the body where it is extracted from the gross part (which is subsequently exhaled through the lungs) in the heart. This active portion is then carried around the body in the circulation of the blood.
122. *Tractatus Secundus De Naturae Simia seu Technica macrocosmi historia* (2nd ed., Frankfort, 1624), 471–72.
123. *De Supernaturali*, 138.

124. *Integrum Morborum Mysterium: Sive Medicinae Catholicae Tomi Primi Tractatus Secundus* (Frankfort, 1631), 456–57, 497–98.

125. For a description of this instrument many of Fludd's writings might be consulted, but he devotes a considerable amount of space describing it in English in his *Mosaicall Philosophy*, 2–9. Fludd does not claim that he invented this instrument. Rather, he states that he learned of it through a manuscript 500 years old. Henry C. Bolton, *Evolution of the Thermometer, 1592–1743* (Easton, Pa., 1900), 27–28, states that this is nothing other than the Galilean thermoscope. Fludd suggested in the above reference that the instrument should be used for measuring the temperature.

126. *Mosaicall Philosophy*, 82.

127. *Ibid.*, 100.

128. *Ibid.*, 203. Fludd discusses the work of Gilbert also in *ibid.*, 213 f., the *Utriusque Cosmi* (1617), 153–58, where he specifically rejects the claims of Gilbert and Copernicus in astronomical thought, and he attacks again the concept of the motion of the earth in his *Clavis Philosophiae et Alchymiae Fluddanae* (Frankfort, 1633), 28.

129. *Mosaicall Philosophy*, 226.

130. For Fludd's views on disease see Pagel, "Religious Motives", 273–82.

131. *Ibid.*, 278.

132. Pagel has discussed Fludd's views in detail on this topic. A few specific references for various points of interest in Fludd's writings are as follows: Fludd discusses the humors in general in his summary to his work in *De Supernaturali*, 200–03. He specifically discusses the humors as the microcosmic elements in the *Medicina Catholica* (1629), 110f., and one of his famous diagrams of man being protected in health by angels who are attacked from without is found in the same work with an explanation, fols. 2 ff. Again he amplifies his views on this subject in *ibid.*, 169.

133. Daniel Sennert, *The Weapon-Salves Maladie* (London, 1637), 4f.

134. William Foster, *Hoplocrisma-Spongus: Or, a Sponge to wipe away the Weapon Salve* (London, 1631), 13–15. The comparison of the name of Paracelsus and a magical spell is most likely taken over by Foster from John Donne's *Ignatius his Conclave* (1611).

135. Foster, *op. cit.*, 33 f.

136. *Ibid.*, 38.

137. *Ibid.*, 39.

138. Fludd, *Fludds Answer*, 41.

139. *Ibid.*, 17. Fludd dealt with so many occult topics that in one of his works he had felt it necessary to explain that he was not a magician even before anyone had made such an accusation. *Utriusque Cosmi* (1617), *Tr. Prima*, Section 2, Part 4, Lib. 3, 98.

140. The controversy appeared to end at this time but in 1633 James Hart referred to the Foster-Fludd dispute in a very detailed attack on Fludd. James Hart, *ΚΛΙΝΙΚΗ* (London, 1633), 361–82. In 1637 an anonymous person

approving of Foster's arguments but deploring his attitude toward Fludd published Sennert's reasons for rejecting the Weapon Salve. See Sennert, *op. cit.*

141. Fludd, *Fludds Answer*, 41.

142. Fludd mentions Paracelsus specifically in the following places: in the *De Naturae Simia*, Part 10, "De Astrologia", 558–714, he quotes him as an authority on charms; in the *De Supernaturali*, 203, he reconciles the Paracelsian three principles with his own primary three elements; he refers to Paracelsus in the *Mosaicall Philosophy*, *passim*, 200–60, in the part of the work dealing with sympathy and the Weapon Salve; and he praises Paracelsus along with all the others attacked by Foster for his work on the Weapon Salve, *Fludds Answer*, 41. Mersenne had pointedly attacked him as a Paracelsian, but Fludd refused to answer this Paracelsian charge in his *Sophiae Cum Moria Certamen* (Frankfort, 1629), 35–38. He specifically objected to Mersenne's attack on Paracelsus in the *Summum Bonum* (Frankfort, 1629), 27. Again he referred to him in the passage explaining the colors on the basis of the three principles, *Medicina Catholica* (1629), 153. And he lauded Paracelsus in the *Pulsus Seu Nova et Arcana Pulsuum Historia* (Frankfort?, 1631?), 81.

143. See, for instance, the *de Praeternaturali*, 123.

144. Pierre Gassendi, *Examen Philosophiae Roberti Fluddi Medici*, in *Opera, 3,* "Opuscula Philosophica" (Lyons, 1658), 211–68, 224.

145. The pertinent Kepler texts are the Appendix to the *Harmonices Mundi* (1619), and the *Apologia Pro Opere Harmonices Mundi Adversus Demonstrationem CL. V. D. Roberti de Fluctibus Medici Oxoniensis* (1622). Both works are conveniently available in Johannes Kepler, *Gesammelte Werke*, ed. Max Caspar (6, Munich, 1940). Note should be taken also of Wolfgang Pauli's "The Influence of Archetypal Ideas on the Scientific Theories of Kepler", tr. Priscilla Silz, included in C. G. Jung and W. Pauli, *The Interpretation of Nature and the Psyche* (New York, 1955), 151–240.

146. Francis Bacon, *Works*, eds. James Spedding, Robert L. Ellis and D. D. Heath, 4 (London, 1870), 403.

147. *Summum Bonum*, 26. Gassendi complained as well that "accommodari ipse vult omnia operationibus chymicis", Gassendi, *Opera Omnia, 3,* 213.

148. *Clavis Philosophiae et Alchymiae Fluddanae*, 56.

149. Foster, 37.

150. *Fludd's Answer*, 21f.

151. Ian. Iacobus Boissard, *Bibliotheca sive Thesaurus Virtutis et Gloriae* (2, Frankfort, 1630), 198.

152. Fuller, *op. cit.*, 281.

153. The only works ascribed to Paracelsus, and now considered spurious, in the 1600–40 period were the reprints of Hester's *Key of Philosophie* [retitled *The Secrets of Physick and Philosophy* (London, 1633), and as an appendix to the works of John Banister (London, 1663)].

Chapter Four

Chemistry and Medicine, 1600-1640

WHEN we turn from alchemical speculations on the macrocosm and the microcosm to the actual laboratory work of the period we enter a different world. In practical matters the iatrochemists were most active in two fields: the promotion of chemically prepared medicines, and the application of analytical methods to the investigation of mineral waters. The first of these was to make chemistry until late in the seventeenth century primarily an art for the pharmacist in the eyes of many physicians, and the second was to lay the foundation of qualitative chemical analysis. And as Paracelsus borrowed freely from earlier philosophical systems for his alchemical cosmology, so too the medieval medical alchemy strongly influenced these practical phases of iatrochemical development.

We have already noted the early and widespread acceptance of chemistry as an aid to medicine. This may be reconciled with the contemporary controversy over chemical innovations only if one recalls the fairly general distrust of strictly "Paracelsian" thought and nostrums among seventeenth-century physicians. Few doctors of repute in England seriously considered Paracelsian speculative cosmology, but the benefits of chemical medicines were utilized by all. In the early years of the seventeenth century the most common tendency was for physicians to rely on both the Galenic corpus and the more recent "Gesnerian-Paracelsian" corpus for the most useful remedies in each. Typical of this approach are the opinions of William Clowes and John Cotta referred to earlier. This was also the view of Thomas Russel, who wrote in 1602 that

betwixt these two extremes [the Galenists and the Paracelsians] I thinke it best to hold a meane, so that I neither allow the extremitie of one, nor imbrace the defects of the other: but mine opinion is, that both the sorts of medicinable preparations of simples, as well that which is done by the Apothecaries craft as also by the Spagiricall art, I say, both of them have their proper place and necessary uses in Phisick (*amicus Plato, amicus Aristoteles, sed magis amica veritas*) so that I iudge this latter age of the world much bound to the careful searchers out of those hiddẽ secrets of nature, which are so bound up in minerals and vegetables, and outwardly do not appear but by extraction and magisterie, and great folly it were utterly to reiect them as many wilfully doe.[a]

But since chemical methods were employed by quacks as well as by sincere chemists it was necessary to distinguish carefully between the "true" and the "false" chemists. In practice this often meant that a respectable London physician intended two different things when he referred to the chemists and to the Paracelsians. The first group (for him) included those pharmacists who prepared the chemical remedies he was willing to accept, while the others were those occult theoreticians and quacks who should be driven from the shores of the island. The empirics were thus constantly under attack for their "improper" use of chemistry. Similarly the pharmacists were watched by the members of the Royal College of Physicians. Under various acts of the sixteenth century their Censors had been given the right to examine the wares of the apothecaries, and the need for some sort of official pharmacopoeia was increasingly evident.

The interest of physicians in chemistry may have been predominantly in pharmacy, but chemical methods were being increasingly applied to other fields as well. The traditional

---

[a] Thomas Russel, *Diacatholicon Aureum: or a generall powder of Gold, purging all offensive humours in mans bodie* (London, 1602), sig. A2.

interest of doctors in mineral water analyses became an obvious field of investigation for the iatrochemists, and their results were to form the basis for modern qualitative analysis. Somewhat less successful were the attempts made to apply chemical techniques to urinalysis and geological problems at this time.

The exponents of traditional alchemy were responsible for little of the advance made. There had been relatively little interest in gold-making in Elizabethan and Jacobean England. Although the Virgin Queen had supported Cornelius Alvetanus in his alchemical projects temporarily, she had been soon disillusioned, and judging from the handful of tracts published on this topic, the public felt much as the Queen did.[1] Even the new interest in mystical alchemy found few supporters in England. The tracts of Timothy Willis and Bishop Thornborough were ignored by their contemporaries, while the only Englishman of international reputation in this field, Robert Fludd, found himself accused of witchcraft at home.

The alchemists suffered as well from their habitual custom of attacking their fellow adepts. The anonymous translator of Lambi's *Revelation* had ridiculed those London alchemists who thought that the philosopher's stone was nothing but common glass.[2] Arthur Dee, who had been trained in the occult sciences as a boy by his father, also complained of the fraudulent and ignorant practisers of the art. In the preface to his *Fasciculus Chemicus* (completed in Moscow in March, 1629) he recalled that as a young student he

found men, (otherwise Learned) unlearned in this Art; amongst which I knew a Bishop, (whose fame in Chymistry was celebrated of many, whom I visited after I had seen a little Chymical Tract, writ with his own hand:) And when I took him laboring in our common Gold, when he studied to extract Vitriol, (which he held his onely Secret) I left him; for that I saw he had neither before him the proper Matter, nor the manner of Working, according to the Doctrine of Philosophers.[3]

Surely this is a thinly veiled attack on the venerable Bishop of Worcester. The alchemists were divided among themselves, and although they borrowed some concepts from their Paracelsian contemporaries, in reality they belonged to an older and more obscure tradition.

The Distinction between the True and the False Chemists

To see the real impact of the new ideas we must turn to the apothecaries, the surgeons, and the physicians—the men who had eagerly adopted many of the new medicines in the last quarter of the sixteenth century. The successors of John Hester continued to promote chemical remedies in the new century, while the followers of the Elizabethan surgeons maintained their earlier enthusiasm for the Paracelsian wound plasters, ointments, and opiates. The surgeons and apothecaries had been won over to the new medicine at an early date, but even in the more conservative Royal College of Physicians the members had planned to prepare an official pharmacopoeia with sections on chemical remedies as early as 1585. The attitude of these men is important, for although they were willing to grant official recognition to some chemical remedies, they were ever on guard against those who peddled chemical compositions which were advertised as universal cures.

The authority of the Royal College of Physicians was very considerable in the opening years of the new century. Founded in 1518 by Henry VIII, its members originally had the right to examine—and therefore control—all surgeons and physicians who practiced in London or within seven miles of the city.[4] Later Acts continued to increase this power. In 1540 the physicians were permitted to include surgery in their practice since this was considered to be basically a part of the study of medicine. At the same time the Company of Barber-Surgeons was founded and it was reaffirmed that no surgeon could practice medicine in London without obtaining a College license. These were not easy to obtain, but some limited licenses were issued. One of those so privileged was the well-known John Banister.[5] In the same year the College was given authority over the apothecaries, for the Censors of the College were empowered to enter their homes "to search, view, and see such Apothecary-wares, drugs and stuffs".[6] This statute was reconfirmed by Queen Mary thirteen years later.[7]

In 1543 another statute was issued which modified the original grants. With a shortage of trained physicians in the country many people living in rural areas were forced to turn to untrained local residents who were thought to have a special knowledge of herbs, or to travelling medicine men. The Act of 1543 took cognizance of this situation and allowed

every person being the King's subject having knowledge and experience of the Nature of herbs, roots and waters . . . [to] use and minister, . . . according to their cunning, experience and knowledge.[8]

With this Act the way was left open for all sorts of empirics to practice in England, since the only judge of their "knowledge and experience" was their own conscience. These persons were limited to prescribing external remedies except for drinks for the stone and a few other ailments.

The Royal College of Physicians waged a constant war on any of these empirics who might venture into the London area. Many of these hated quacks adopted the name "Paracelsian" and prescribed metallic or mineral remedies, but the members of the College were generally aware of the difference between them and the sincere practitioners who wished to utilize the best of the new and the old medicines: Thomas Moffett had strongly advocated the use of chemical remedies and he had become an esteemed member of the College, while even the belligerent Robert Fludd had been admitted to their company.

This distinction between the "true Paracelsian" and the "false Paracelsian" has already been mentioned in the work of the surgeons and physicians of the late sixteenth century,[9] and it was to become a familiar theme in the next century as well. The College regularly sought out the alchemical empirics, halted their practice, and fined them heavily. Among the men so prosecuted was the young Arthur Dee, who had settled in London in 1603 to practice medicine. He offended the medical authorities by exhibiting on his door a list of medicines which he guaranteed as certain cures for many diseases.[10]

Far more significant was the prosecution of Francis Anthony. Born in 1550, Anthony had received the M.A. at Cambridge in 1574 but it is unknown whether or not he later obtained the M.D. degree. A self-styled Paracelsian, he was an empiric and chemical physician who had an international reputation for his *aurum potabile*. However, both as the promoter of this cure-all and because of his unlicensed status, he was vulnerable to the attack of the College on two counts. He first came to the attention of the Censors of the College in 1598 for promoting cures in London with his gold remedies. In Charles Goodall's *History of the College* (1684) there is a relation of the conflict between Anthony and this organization in the first ten years of the century.[11] The matter came to a head in 1610 when Anthony published his *Medicinae Chymiae*. In this work he referred repeatedly to Paracelsus, Duchesne, Penotus, and other leading iatrochemists. In essence he had set out to prove that metals were the most important of all remedies and that since gold is the most noble of all metals, it must also be the most noble of all medicines.[12] He admitted that gold was a difficult metal to obtain in solution, but he affirmed that by proper calcination it could be done and that *aurum potabile* could thus be prepared.[13] A formula for this process ascribed to Anthony was published in the *Collectanea Chymica* (1684).[14] It amounts to little more than an attempt to react the vinegar of wine with finely powdered gold. From this Anthony contended that a thick syrup would result.

Unlike many other empirics, Anthony was an outstanding publicist and his work attracted wide attention. It was soon attacked by a member of the Royal College of Physicians: Matthew Gwinne, a fellow of the College from 1605 until his death in 1627 and six times a Censor during that time, rushed into print with a scholarly refutation of Anthony's tract.[15] He contended that Anthony's *aurum potabile* (or as he called it, *aurum putabile*) contained no gold, but even if it did, he did not think that its virtues as a medicine corresponded with its value as a metal. He noted that Libavius in quoting Paracelsus confirmed the fact that gold cannot be dissolved except with the use of a highly corrosive acid which would render it unfit for medicinal purposes.[16] Gwinne's work is for the most part erudite. From the authorities cited it is plain that although his viewpoint was strongly Galenist, he had read the chief works of the Paracelsians as well. Occasionally he lashed out at his adversaries in the rough manner of the day, as when he called the chemists "impostors", "tricksters", and "rascals",[17] but it is significant that he separated the "chymici" from the "Chemiatrae" or the "Galenochymici" among whom he wished to be classed himself.[18] This is another case where even an admittedly conservative member of the College wished to distinguish between the sincere and the fraudulent chemists.

It is interesting to note that Francis Anthony was attacked by the chemists as well as by the Censors of the College. Thomas Rawlin had had an earlier career much like Anthony's. He had been awarded the M.A. degree at Oxford and after coming to London in 1596 was prosecuted by the College and fined forty pounds for practicing unlawfully. The following year he was also in trouble for compounding medicinal drinks.[19] However, in 1610 he chose to refute Anthony's tract in his *Admonitio Pseudo-Chymicis seu Alphabetarium Philosophicum*. Like Gwinne, Rawlin cited his sources constantly and his relatively short work contains well over 600 marginal notations. A large percentage of these are from alchemical and Paracelsian authors, Raymon Lull being quoted no less than 87 times and Paracelsus 35 times. Rawlin states that the fruits of alchemy are obtained both by the "sweatings" of body and mind and by the gift of God.[20] Only the pseudo-chemists desire gold, and all true alchemists realize that the purpose of their science is to obtain the health of mankind. In making this distinction he clearly classed Anthony among the pseudo-chemists or the empirics.

In 1616 Francis Anthony replied with an *Apology* which was published simultaneously in Latin and English. This was made up primarily from testimonials sent to him from people he claimed to have cured.[21] John Cotta (whose *Short Discoverie* was discussed in Chapter 2) answered this *Apology*. In his *Cotta Contra Antonium: or an Ant-Antony*, he was willing to class *aurum potabile* among other cordials, but he was most indignant with Anthony for the universal cures he claimed for his medicine. Cotta even suggested that such claims were similar to those of witchcraft.[22] His work was the last exchange in this controversy, since Anthony died the year Cotta's tract was published (1623).

Of all the chemical empirics whom the members of the Royal College had prosecuted none had gained such inter-national renown as Anthony. His recipe for the *aurum potabile* was considered a secret of such value that it was included in the *Collectanea Chymica* of 1684, but much earlier Robert Burton had referred to him in the *Anatomy of Melancholy* for his espousal of potable gold. He mentioned that "Rhenanus, a Dutch chemist, in his book *de sale e puteo emergente*, takes upon him to apologize for Anthony, and sets light by all that speak against him".[23] Similarly, Helvig Dieterich, a German Paracelsian, praised Anthony's health-giving solution in 1627.[24]

The Anthony case shows that even when dealing with the most obstinate men the English physicians tried to distinguish between two types of chemists. There was a general agreement that sincere chemists should not be classed with those charlatans who masked their frauds behind a façade of alchemical termino-logy and equipment. This distinction was made often by men of differing opinions and it would be impossible to find a definition which would have been acceptable to all of them. Thus in the Anthony case Gwinne quite heartily condemned the

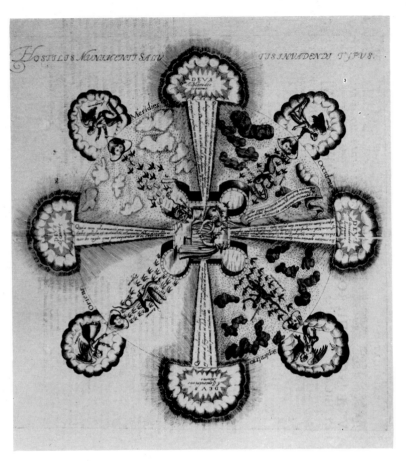

PLATE 5. *Disease pictured as an invasion of man's "castle of health".*
From the frontispiece material in Fludd's Integrum Morborum
Mysterium: sive Medicinae Catholicae. Tomi Primi, Tractatus
Secundus *(Frankfort, 1631). (Courtesy Houghton Library, Harvard*
University.)

PLATE 6. *The analysis of a mineral water in the sixteenth century. From Conrad Gesner's* The Newe Jewell of Health, *translated by Thomas Hill and George Baker (London, 1576), folio 41, verso. (Courtesy Houghton Library, Harvard University.)*

chemists as impostors but was willing to accept the "Galeno-chemists". Thomas Rawlin, on the other hand, as a chemist himself, only wished to draw a line between the true chemists and the pseudo-chemists. Similarly, somewhat later Thomas Brugis was perfectly willing to recommend Paracelsus as an authority in medicine and surgery[25] and to use various mineral and metallic remedies,[26] but he warned his readers against

Mountebanks, Empiricks, Quacksalvers, Paracelsians (as they call themselves) Wizards, Alcumists, Poor-vicars, cast Apothecaries, and Physitians men, Barbers, and Good-wives that professe great skill, go with the name of Doctor, which title perhaps they bought at some beyond-sea University, where they bestow this degree upon such people for their money; the phrase they use is Accipiamus pecuniam, demittamus asinum, and so with this title of Doctorasse, away he flyes into all countries possessing the people with stories and false tales.[27]

This conflict also makes clear the opposition of the members of the College to universal cures. From the cases reported by Goodall, this was a major point considered in any judgment of chemists. Men such as Thomas Moffett and Robert Fludd had made no such sweeping claims for the newer medicines—that Anthony had done so was considered one of his major offenses.[28]

The Pharmacopoeia of 1618

The use of Paracelsian remedies in medical recipe books had been common since Elizabethan times. One of the best known of these Elizabethan collections was the *Antidotarie Chyrurgicall* of John Banister (1589).[29] Here some thirty-five references to Paracelsus, Duchesne, and Thurneisser had been placed side by side with quotations from older and less controversial authors. Banister's quiet acceptance of these new authorities had been an early indication of the general trend among English physicians and surgeons, and his influence was in evidence in the new century through the works of his grandson Stephen Bradwell.[30] Bradwell published a series of small tracts in the 1630s[31] in which he claimed that he alone possessed the secret formulae for his grandfather's most potent remedies. At the same time (1633) Thomas Harper published in one volume the complete works of Banister. Here he included a reprint of Hester's translation of the *Keys of Philosophy* (1575) from which he deleted Hester's introductory autobiographical material.[32] William Lugger also printed the *Keys* in 1633 as the *Secrets of Philosophy*.

The Elizabethan custom of listing together recipes culled from the recent and the ancient authors continued in the new century. John Wood had felt no inconsistency in citing Erastus next to Paracelsus,[33] and the continually revised sixteenth-century *English-Mans Treasure* of Thomas Vicary had much of its space devoted to chemical remedies by the time it went into its eighth edition in 1633. The collection of Thomas Bonham included receipts from the most controversial of the Paracelsians as well as the ancients.[34]

The acceptance of chemical medicines was generally approved of by the doctors and surgeons of the new century. It is difficult to find many authors who opposed the new medicines, but the case of James Hart, a dedicated anti-Paracelsian, may be cited.[35] In his *ΚΛΙΝΙΚΗ* (1633) he declared that it was false to affirm that metals nourish the body, and he specifically pointed out that they fail as antidotes against the plague.[36] He attacked Paracelsus and his followers because of their belief in the power of fascination, and he devoted an entire chapter to a refutation of Fludd's work on the Weapon Salve.[37] For him such views made Paracelsus suspect of practicing magic,[38] and he laughed at the Paracelsians who promised the prolongation of life far beyond the age of 100 to 120 by the use of gold and other metallic medicines:

. . . although this great miracle-monger (as his foolish followers would make him) died (not without tormenting arthriticall paines many times, notwithstanding all his secrets) before hee attained the 60th yeere of his age, yet will not their folly depart from them if they were braied in a mortar, affirming him yet to live in his grave by vertue of aurum potabile, writing great voluminous bookes, and inditing many profitable precepts to his disciples. I hope the Printers shall not want work when they are ready.[39]

This was a common criticism of Paracelsus in the first half of the seventeenth century. Henry Cuffe (1607) had said that Paracelsus died before he was thirty,[40] and only Sir William Vaughn (1630) correctly stated that he had died at the age of forty-eight.[41] In comparison with this short life Vaughn observed that Hippocrates and Galen had lived until they were past one hundred, leaving it to the reader to judge which system was the best to follow.

If it is difficult to locate any wholesale condemnation of metallic and mineral remedies in this period, it is also hard to find any authors who advocated mineral remedies alone. Francis Anthony had affirmed this, but he must be classed more as an empiric—or even a charlatan—than a true Paracelsian. We have already considered the anonymous *Philiatros* (1615) and John Woodall's *Surgions Mate* (1617), both of which strongly supported the value of the new medicines without, however, discarding the ancient corpus. The two Hester reprints of the *Secrets of Philosophy* (1633) urged the adoption of mineral drugs and distilled vegetable products, but besides these, the major work in this period to uphold chemical medicines as far more efficacious than the traditional ones was Angelo Sala's *Opiologia*, translated by Thomas Bretnor M.M. and published in London in 1618. In his preface Sala questions "whether Chymicall Medicines in generall are more violent than other ordinary medicines are; and whether in respect thereof a man may lawfully administer them except in desperate diseases onely as some imagine?"[42] In his answer Sala notes that there are some physicians who do not entirely condemn chemical medicines "as not long since many did". However, they say that these preparations are of varying value and that they are usually more violent and dangerous than the traditional ones; such authors therefore insist that chemical medicines should only be used in desperate cases. Sala replies that by arguing in this fashion these men unwittingly condemn many medicines used both by the Spagyrists and the Galenists. The latter center their attack on the violent effects produced in the body by "Antimonie and Mercury vomative" but Sala answers that these are in reality quite gentle compared to the traditional emetics like Hellebore and Tythimalis. Fire purges the medicines of their gross qualities and makes it possible to isolate the health-giving substance, and so chemically prepared substances are "far more apt to worke" than the Galenic remedies. And if it should be objected that the greater subtility of these medicines means that they are more likely to disturb the proper balance of nature, truly there are some diseases which require such a remedy. But beyond all other arguments, the real proof of the importance of chemistry for medicine is the fact that by chemical means poisons may be so altered that they can be safely administered in fairly large doses.[43]

Occasionally one meets a reference in an English work to the quarrel between the Chemists and the Galenists, but it is either qualified as in Cotta's *Short Discoverie* (1612)[44] and Gwinne's refutation of Anthony (1611), or else it occurs in a work for popular consumption such as *The Anatomy of Melancholy* where Burton states:

Let Paracelsus, Quercetan, Crollius, and the brethren of the Rosy Cross defend themselves as they may. Crato, Erastus, and the Galenists oppugn Paracelsus; he brags on the other side, he did more famous cures by this means than all the Galenists in Europe, and calls himself a monarch; Galen, Hippocrates, infants, illiterate, etc. As Thessalus of old railed against Asclepidean writers, "he condemns others, insults, triumphs, overcomes, all antiquity" (saith Galen as if he spake to him), "declares himself a conqueror, and crowns his own doings." "One drop of their chemical preparations shall do more good than all their fulsome potions." (Codronchus) Erastus and the rest of the Galenists vilify them on the other side, as heretics in physic: "Paracelsus did that in physic, which Luther in divinity." (*idem*) "A drunken rogue he was, a base fellow, a magician, he had the devil for his master, devils his familiar companions, and what he did was done by the help of the devil." (Erastus) Thus they contend and rail, and every mart write books pro and con, *et adhuc sub judice lis est* (and the case is still proceeding): let them agree as they will, I proceed.[45]

In spite of Burton's opinion, there were far fewer controversial works on this topic than in the period prior to 1600. After the death of John Hester in the 1590s there had been no one to take his place as a translator of Paracelsian recipe collections. The translation of Sala's *Opiologia* by Thomas Bretnor in 1618 is the only tract similar to the older output of Hester. On the other hand there were no militant Galenist works either. Most collected works continued in the Elizabethan tradition—some might adhere more strongly than others to the ancient medicines and a few might emphasize the compiler's interest in the newer chemical remedies, but the great majority borrowed freely from both sources without any hint of contradiction.

However, the custom of publishing private collections of medical receipts had been noted with alarm even in the Elizabethan period. It is true that the Statutes of 1540 and 1553 had given the Royal College of Physicians the power to enter and inspect the shops of apothecaries. But without an official pharmacopoeia it was not easy to supervise their wares. The Elizabethan apothecary could turn to ancient authors or to recent collections ranging from the Paracelsian translations of Hester to the more conservative herbalists. In the sixteenth century William Bullein was recommending as indispensable for the apothecary the collections of "Nicolaus Myrepsi, Valerius Cordos, Iohanne's *Placaton* ye Lubik, etc.". At the same time Robert Recorde required Cordus and Myrepsius plus the *Dispensatory* of Bernardus Dessenius, the *De Stirpium* of Leonardus Fuchsius, and many others.[46] There was a need for an official pharmacopoeia, but in the late sixteenth century there were very few of these.[47] Those that were in use were enforced only over small geographical areas. The first had been the *Nuovo Receptario Composito* at Florence (1498). This had been followed half a century later by pharmacopoeias at Nuremberg (1546), Augsburg (1564), and Cologne (1565). Of these the most important was the *Pharmacopoeia Augustana* which was the first to include distilled products. Professor Urdang has shown that the few chemical preparations in the 1564 edition were limited to external use, but that these were considerably augmented in the 1613 edition, where for the first time were included chemical remedies which could be used internally.[48]

When, therefore, the members of the Royal College of Physicians began to discuss the possibility of issuing their own pharmacopoeia in 1585, they were undertaking an important project. In 1589 an outline of the proposed pharmacopoeia was prepared and committees were assigned to the different divisions. In keeping with the Elizabethan approach one of the proposed sections was reserved for chemical medicine. And it was fitting that Thomas Moffett who had defended these remedies in print should be assigned to this committee. The other two members were Christopher Johnson (d. 1597) and the influential Thomas Langton (president of the College from 1604 until his death in 1606).[49] Unfortunately the findings of this group are no longer extant and the whole project seems to have been shelved shortly thereafter.

This official approval of the new medicines in England may be contrasted with the struggle between the Paracelsians and the Galenists then going on in France.[50] At the opening of the seventeenth century the Galenist medical faculty at Paris had the right to limit practitioners in the city to Paris graduates. The other great French medical school, Montpellier, was at the same time becoming more and more oriented towards the iatrochemists. Gradually graduates from southern France were moving to Paris, where they used metallic remedies in their practice, to the great annoyance of the members of the Parisian faculty. The most vociferous of the Parisian iatrochemists were Joseph Duchesne and Theodore Turquet de Mayerne. The great impact of Duchesne's works on Elizabethan and Jacobean physicians has already been noted. As a Protestant he had obtained his M.D. degree at Basle in 1573, but he did not move to Paris until appointed physician to Henry IV in 1593. Ten years later he published his *De materia verae medicinae philosophorum priscorum*, in which he upheld the three principles and opposed the doctrines and remedies of the Galenists. It is not surprising that this work was almost immediately condemned by the faculty at Paris.

At this point Duchesne found an ally in Theodore Turquet de Mayerne, who like Duchesne was a Protestant.[51] Mayerne's father had fled with his family to Geneva after the St. Bartholomew's Day Massacre in 1572, and there Theodore was born in the following year. He attended Heidelberg and then Montpellier, where he took his M.D. degree in 1597. Shortly after this he moved to Paris, where he too became physician in ordinary to the King. Two years later he began lecturing on iatrochemistry to young surgeons and apothecaries at Paris. His opinions were already well known when he published his *Apologia in qua videre est inviolatis Hippocratis et Galenis legibus, remedia chymice preparata, tuto usurpare posse* (1603) after the condemnation of Duchesne's work. This time it was Mayerne's turn to be proscribed. The faculty forbade his colleagues to consult with him and urged the King to rescind his public offices. However, Henry IV ignored this physicians' quarrel and went on to grant Mayerne further honors.

In 1606 he had the luck to cure an influential Englishman who had become ill in France. After his cure the grateful patient invited his physician to come with him to England; the offer was accepted and Mayerne found himself honored in London by being appointed one of the physicians to the Queen. Nevertheless, he returned to France, where he remained until the assassination of Henry IV in 1610. At this time James I summoned him from Paris. Once again in London, he was now appointed the chief physician to the King and his household, a post he retained until his death in 1655.

With his high position it would have been strange if Turquet de Mayerne had not furthered the cause of iatrochemistry in

England. Actually there is evidence to show that he did much of the work on the first edition of the *Pharmacopoeia Londinensis* although he was not made a member of the Royal College of Physicians until 1616. The revival of interest in the abandoned pharmacopoeia, however, was due less to him than to Henry Atkins, who was instrumental in reactivating the project in 1614.[52]

The actual publication of this *Pharmacopoeia* was closely allied with the problems involved in supervising the apothecaries. The pharmacists had been incorporated for the first time in 1606, when James I had granted a joint charter to the apothecaries and grocers.[53] This venture suited neither group, and in 1617 Atkins and Mayerne succeeded in persuading the King to grant the apothecaries a separate charter, under which they were to dispense but not prescribe medicines. By this time the official *Pharmacopoeia* was nearing publication: it was intended to serve as a guide not only for doctors in their prescriptions, but also for apothecaries in the compounding of these medicines.

The first edition of the work was issued in May, 1618. Due to conflicts within the College the May issue was recalled and a second edition, somewhat enlarged, was issued later in the year. For our purpose it is most important to note that the author of the preface "Candido Lectori" (probably Mayerne) wrote that

we venerate the age old learning of the ancients and for this reason we have placed their remedies at the beginning, but on the other hand, we neither reject nor spurn the new subsidiary medicines of the more recent chemists and we have conceded to them a place and corner in the rear so that they might be as a servant to the dogmatic medicine, and thus they might act as auxiliaries.[54]

Thus this *Pharmacopoeia* is clearly representative of the compromise attitude characteristic of English physicians for the forty-year period prior to its publication.[55]

The second edition of 1618 was to remain the official one with few variations for many years, and even the second London *Pharmacopoeia* of 1650 maintained the sections on chemical remedies with few alterations. These chemical divisions, the *Sales, Metallica, Mineralia*, the *Olea Chymica*, and the *Praeparationes Chymicae Magis Usuales*, consisted of a series of preparations culled from ancient and modern authors which varied little from one edition to the next in this period. We may see this more clearly in a numerical breakdown of the number of preparations in these various editions.[56]

Date of Publication	2nd ed. 1618	1627	1638	1650
Sales, Metallica, Mineralia	85	101	91	87
Olea Chymica	20	23	23	22
Praeparationes Chymicae Magis Usuales	17	18	19	21

From the first category Urdang has shown that most of the minerals and metals were taken from Dioscorides.[57] Among the "Chemical Oils" there were only a few which involved real chemical reactions rather than simple distillations of a crude substance. The most important preparations in this section include *oleum antimonii* ($SbCl_3$), *oleum salis* (HCl), *oleum sulphuris* (H_2SO_3), *liquor tartari vulgo oleum tartari dictum* (K_2CO_3), *oleum vitrioli* (H_2SO_4), *aqua fortis* (HNO_3), and *oleum arsenici* (potassium arsenate). Even among the "more usual chemical preparations" many of the recipes are for mixtures which involve no chemical processes. Many of the compounds were well known to the earlier alchemists or to contemporary Paracelsians. Thus the *saccharum saturni* was known to Libavius while the three antimony preparations, *crocus metallorum, mercurius vitae*, and *vitrum antimonii*, were among the best known of the Paracelsian remedies. *Tartarus vitriolatus* (K_2SO_4) was taken from Oswald Croll's Paracelsian pharmacopoeia, the *Basilica Chymica*. Turquet de Mayerne was indebted to Croll also for his directions for *Mercurius dulcis* or calomel, which was one of the most recent remedies to be found in this work.

Although authorities for many medicinal preparations were

cited throughout the rest of the volume, this was seldom done in the chemical sections. Urdang has suggested that the reason for this was that the open use of these controversial modern authors would have given rise to complaints. He has pointed to the fact that Mayerne noted in his copy of the second edition of 1618 that he had obtained the formula for *Mercurius dulcis* from Croll,[58] but that this does not appear in the printed version. Furthermore, Paracelsus was cited only once in this volume and then only in regard to his famed "Stipticum" or wound plaster.[59] Thus the members were willing to recognize Paracelsus as a famous surgeon but not as the controversial leader of the chemists. This interpretation by Urdang fits in well with the earlier history of the Elizabethan physicians. From the first the physicians and the surgeons had been willing to utilize chemistry and any chemically prepared remedies of value, but Paracelsus himself continued to be looked on with deep-rooted suspicion.

This publication was the first great national pharmacopoeia. Its influence was considerable and there was a noticeable slackening of interest in the private collections of remedies after 1618. However, for those who preferred a collection of receipts slanted more toward the chemical preparations there were the Banister and Hester reprints of 1633 already referred to, while evidence of apothecaries who specialized in such remedies is afforded by the price list of remedies for sale published by D. Gordon in Aberdeen in 1625.[60] This author complained of those who had laughed at him because of his interest in alchemy,[61] and he listed a large number of "Chymicall Medicaments" which he had available or could make on order.[62] These included common distilled waters, distilled cordial or composed waters, spirits, a variety of distilled chemical oils, tinctures, extracts, calcined substances, salts, and sublimed substances. On the other hand, for those who preferred a more conservative pharmacopoeia, there was Philemon Holland's Latin translation of the extremely popular *Pharmacopoea* of Brice Bauderon

(1639). Until this date Bauderon's work had only been available in French, and Holland's Latin translation was designed to make it more easily available to English physicians. The preface was composed by the anti-Paracelsian surgeon, Alexander Read, and the general tone of the treatise is far more conservative than the *Pharmacopoeia Londinensis*. Even under the opiates there is no mention of any Paracelsian drugs, and only at the end of the volume did Bauderon add a reference to "Laudanum Spagyricum" and the well-known "Emplastrum Paracelsis", neither of which he recommended.[63]

Urdang has shown that the publication of the *Pharmacopoeia Londinensis* should not be considered revolutionary since most of its newer remedies were already to be found in the 1613 edition of the *Pharmacopoeia Augustana*. This latter work also antedated the London collection in the prescription of these chemical remedies for internal use. However, the 1618 editions still retain their importance because they represent the earliest national pharmacopoeias, and because of the evidence they present for the early and official acceptance of chemical remedies. The fact that they represent at best a compromise between the old and the new systems is not unexpected, since this had been the attitude of most members of the College for over thirty years.

The *Pharmacopoeia Londinensis* marks also an increased influence of the Royal College of Physicians. The members had been instrumental in arranging for the separate incorporation of the apothecaries in 1617 and their new publication was to serve primarily as a guide for them to follow. At the same time the members of the College had arranged to obtain a separate charter granting to themselves further powers. The statutes of 1540 and 1553 had given the College the right to search and examine all apothecary wares, and in the Royal Charter of 1618 this was extended to include the "Distillers and Sellers of waters or oyles", as well as the "Preparers of Chymical Medicynes".[64]

The authority which the College exercised—or attempted to

exercise—over the surgeons and the apothecaries was more effectively extended to the distillers in 1638. This profession had been unregulated since the Middle Ages, and once again Theodore Turquet de Mayerne was involved in the founding of a City Company.[65] His purpose in this case was to regulate the distillations then being practiced, but since the apothecaries also were distillers, they felt that their rights were being encroached upon. It is understandable that the history of these companies in the seventeenth century is to a large extent the relation of innumerable disputes over real and imagined privileges.

The Extension of Chemical Methods

The ever increasing application of chemical methods extended beyond the realm of pharmacy in the sixteenth and seventeenth centuries. There was a growing utilization of chemical knowledge in new fields, but since most of those who were interested in chemistry were connected with the medical profession, it is not surprising to find that medical applications were the most common. The great metallurgical and mining texts of Biringuccio, Agricola, and Ercker had been printed during the sixteenth century. These works made available to all chemists the technological processes which had accumulated over the centuries. This information was to become part of the standard lore of the seventeenth-century chemist, but for the most part the processes described in these volumes were not new, and significant advances in metallurgy did not occur until the eighteenth century. For this reason as well as the fact that there were no English contributions to this literature until 1640, the metallurgical technology of the period forms little part of our story.

The medical fields most influenced by chemistry were the analyses of urine and mineral waters. Both of these were topics of great interest to the Continental Paracelsians and their genesis may be found in sources that antedated Paracelsus. Pagel has recently discussed in detail the development of Paracelsian urinalysis[66] and we summarize his conclusions here. Objecting to the belief that diseases could be identified by means of a simple inspection of the patient's urine, Paracelsus called instead for a "chemical dissection" of the sample. Since urine is comprised of waste from the entire body the physician might expect a chemical dissection to give the same information obtained from a bodily dissection. This dissection of urine was nothing more than a distillation to be carried out in a specially gauged cylinder, the shape of which was to correspond to the human body. A careful examination of the various fractions of the distillate as well as the residue was to reveal the type of disease as well as its location in the body. The urine was also to be assessed by its weight, thus bringing into medical practice for the first time a method which is still used today. Under the Paracelsian system the urine with the lowest specific gravity had the greatest amount of salt, while mercurial urine was the heaviest. These views were elaborated in the pseudo-Paracelsian *Anatomia Corporum adhuc viventium* (1st ed. 1577) and various other works by the early Paracelsians—most notably the *Probierung der Harnen* of Thurneisser zum Thurn (1571).

In England these ideas did not gain wide currency, but R. Bostocke condemned traditional uroscopy in 1585. He made no reference to comparisons by specific weight, but he did urge that the distillation procedures of Paracelsus and his followers be adopted.[67] In the early seventeenth century no Englishman wrote in favor of this system, but several physicians attacked those who placed too great a reliance on uroscopy. Among these were John Cotta, Thomas Brian, and James Primerose.[68] None of these authors described the Paracelsian method of urine distillation, but this method was one subject of complaint by James Hart in his *Anatomie of Urine* (1625). Accepting the value of the traditional methods of urine examination for diagnostic purposes, Hart insisted that other symptoms must not be disregarded. Hence, a trained doctor was absolutely essential for the recovery of a sick person. He specifically attacked the Paracelsians for their distillations and weighings of urine and he felt that they spent too much time trying to decide whether the disease was due to an excess of one or another of the three principles rather than attempting to find out what the disease was and where it was located in the body.[69] Hart's treatises on this topic would indicate that even if this doctrine found few supporters in England, at least it was known and discussed.

Far more important for the progress of chemistry was the development of chemical analysis for mineral waters. The analysis of these waters may be traced through a long line of Italian treatises written by Paduan professors of medicine as early as the fourteenth century.[70] At first these investigations had simply involved the evaporation of the sample with the subsequent examination of the residue by the senses, although Giacomo de Dondi (1298–1359) had suggested testing the residue on a red-hot coal to make more noticeable any hidden odors.[71] By the end of the fourteenth century distillation began to replace evaporation as the most popular method of isolating the dissolved substances, and in the following century Michael Savonarola (c. 1390–1462) included in his *De balneis et termis naturalibus omnibus ytalie* a chapter on the analysis of waters. His method called for distillation followed by a careful examination of the residue after it was dried in the sun, where specific substances were to be identified by their sparkle in the light. Further tests were to be made by casting the residue on the fire and noting the odor, any change in the color of the solid, or the color of the flame. (Savonarola knew that sulphur burned with a green flame.)[72]

These Italian works exerted considerable influence, and their tests were augmented in the early sixteenth century from other sources. The gall test as a check for alum or vitriol had been the earliest color indicator and it had been referred to several times by Pliny. However, the earliest reference to it by a Renaissance author seems to be by Paracelsus (c. 1520).[73] Specific gravity was made an important factor in analytical procedures by Georgius Agricola in 1545, but instead of referring to his own evidence for this he spoke in general terms and mentioned ancient accounts of waters which varied greatly in specific gravity over the course of the year.[74]

The reintroduction of the gall test and Agricola's stress on colors and specific gravity is reflected in many works published after 1550. Among them is the most important of the later Italian works on solution analysis—the text on medicated waters by the famous Paduan anatomist, Gabriel Fallopius (1523–63).[75] After distillation of the sample Fallopius suggested that the residue should be spread out thinly in the sun and that the analyst should try to identify any bright crystals which were evident. For further identification some of the residue was to be placed on a red-hot iron. Here he felt that gypsum, lime, marble, sulphur, niter, and salt could be differentiated. He knew of the gall test, which he used as a method of determining either vitriol or alum. Metals were to be determined by acidifying the residue with aqua fortis and examining this second residue after the acid had been distilled.

This book by Fallopius had a far-reaching influence—not so much in its original form as in the lengthy abstract made from it which was included by Conrad Gesner in the second part of his *Treasure of Euonymus*. Gesner's work was very popular and it was soon translated into French (1573), English (1576), and German (1583).

Fallopius was one of the last of the important Italian analysts, but this tradition soon became of considerable interest to the iatrochemists and Paracelsians in the sixteenth century. Paracelsus had revived the gall test as a color indicator and he also wrote a tract on mineral waters. Although his work on this subject was far inferior to the Italian treatises which were available at the time, he did point out that it was important to determine the constituents of these waters.[76]

Among the followers of Paracelsus these analyses were

quickly developed far beyond the works of the Italian authors. Leonhart Thurneisser turned from the chemical analysis of urine (1571) to the analyses of mineral waters in the following year in his *Pison*. Here he introduced quantitative methods, solubility tests, crystallographic evidence, and several flame tests in a more advanced procedure than that of Fallopius. Andreas Libavius also devoted much thought to the analysis of mineral waters in his *Alchemie* of 1597. His process was similar to that of Thurneisser, utilizing the best of the tests of the Italians and emphasizing a quantitative approach to analytical problems. Of particular significance in the work of Thurneisser and Libavius was the attention placed on the recrystallization of the residue from the distillation. This made possible for the first time the use of crystal forms as a means of identification.[77] After Libavius, despite specific emendations, there were no large-scale revisions of these procedures until the time of Robert Boyle.

It is interesting to observe that the first English reference to Paracelsus was made in a work examining the properties of the spa at Bath. This is in the *Booke of the natures and properties as well of the bathes in England as of other bathes in Germanye and Italye*, which was written by the Henrician and Marian exile, William Turner, in 1557. Turner was familiar with the works of Savonarola, Gesner, and Agricola, and he often quoted from them. He seldom discussed analytical problems in detail, but in his description of the Italian baths at Ebanus he quoted directly from Savonarola in a passage which referred to the use of distillation as a means of analysis.[78] Turner himself described how he examined the minerals at Bath. He entered the water and scooped up from the bottom some of the "slyme, mudde, bones, and stones whyche alltogether smelled evidentlye of brimstone". He felt that if anything else was mixed with the sulphur it must be copper since he found marcasite and copper-bearing stones in the nearby hills.[79] Turner employed no chemical methods in his work at Bath but, like Paracelsus, he recognized the importance of the dissolved minerals

PLATE 7. *Portrait of Sir Theodore Turquet De Mayerne.*

and felt that they should be isolated or identified in some manner.

It was not until the translation by Thomas Hill of the second part of Gesner's *Treasure of Euonymus* appeared as *The Newe Jewell of Health* in 1576 that any of the Renaissance developments in analysis were published in English. Here was a true analytical procedure which included a description of the "oak galls test" as a means of identifying both vitriol and alum.[80] The exact influence of this translation is difficult to determine due to the scarcity of sixteenth-century English works on mineral waters, but it is quite likely the text followed by Walter Bailey in his analysis of the waters of Newnam Regis in 1587. Bailey, a physician to Queen Elizabeth, distilled his sample and placed part of the residue on a glowing iron to differentiate between limestone and plaster. He also checked for the presence of salt and niter by listening for the crackling sound made by strongly heated salt. Finally he observed that if common water were dyed black and then poured on this sediment, the dark color would be made clearer. From all this he concluded that there was alum present.[81] All of these tests are described in the texts of Fallopius and Gesner, and Bailey presented them in the same order in which they had originally appeared.

In spite of the description of the gall test in *The Newe Jewell of Health*, there are no further references to color indicators in the English literature until fifty years later—although it should be mentioned that the *Newe Jewell* was reprinted in 1599. This color test figured prominently in the discovery of the spring at Scarborough (1626),[82] and it is described in great detail in the earliest references to Harrogate by Edmund Deane and Michael Stanhope.[83] In these works sulphur was tested by the discoloration it produced on silver, and the dissolved gases or "airey particles" were recognized as an essential part of the water. Analysts therefore were cautioned carefully to stopper any samples if they could not be investigated on the spot.[84]

Far more comprehensive than the work of these men at

Harrogate was the *Discourse of Naturall Bathes, and Minerall Waters* by Edward Jorden, which was printed five times between 1631 and 1673. Jorden (1569–1632) came from a good family but as a younger son he was destined for a profession. He attended Oxford and then travelled abroad and obtained his M.D. at Padua. After his return to England he became a member of the Royal College of Physicians and was named one of the royal physicians himself. At an early age he had associated himself with the latest advances in science, and through him may be seen an English link with the iatrochemical tradition of Thurneisser and Libavius. The latter evidently had been a close friend of his, for in the *Alchemia* of 1597 Libavius had listed Jorden first among certain friends, including Tycho Brahe, who had offered him information for his book.[85] Only a few years later he was called on to investigate a case of demoniac possession which he attributed to natural causes.[86] He rejected transmutation[87] and explained heat as the result of the motion of the "seeds or formes" of a substance.[88] He ridiculed the theory of sympathy and antipathy,[89] and like many other chemists, he considered the motion of the Sun around the earth to be a "monstrous" concept.[90] More interesting was his rejection of the four elements as material substances out of which all things consist.[91] Like Boyle later, Jorden asserted that in analysis by dissolution the four elements are not shown to be present. Rather, he felt that his findings were more in accord with the opinion of Hippocrates and the chemists of his own day.

Jorden praised Agricola, Fallopius, and Libavius for their analytical procedures and he was also familiar with the work of Thurneisser.[92] He attacked authors who relied simply on distillation followed by tasting the residue, stating that this was a thoroughly inadequate method of analysis.[93] As a general check to see if dissolved impurities were present he suggested that the weight of the water be compared with pure water, but he complained "it is hard to have great ballances so exact, as a small difference may be discerned by them".[94]

Jorden divided the ingredients of mineral waters into eight categories: simple earth, stone, bitumen, salts, mineral spirits, mean metals, metals, and spiritual substances.[95] Of these, the most interesting are the salts. He stated that there are four types of salt—niter, salt, alum, and vitriol—and that each of these has diverse species.[96] Jorden's procedure for the identification of salts was based primarily on crystal form. After a stick had been put in the liquor it was allowed to stand and

within a few dayes, the concrete iuyces will shoote upon the wood, in Needles, if it bee Niter; in Squares, if it be Salt; and in Clods and Lumps, if it be Allum or Coperose; and the other minerall substance which the waters have received, will either incorporate a tincture with them, or if it be more terrestriall, will settle and separate from it, and by drying it at a gentle fire will shew from what house it comes, either by colour, taste, smell, or vertue. . . .[97]

Crystal form had been used for identification earlier than this, but it had never before been considered so necessary. Jorden suggested that saltpeter should be tested for purity by crystallization techniques for only when pure will it shoot into needles. When impure it will appear in "squares or angles or lumps".[98] He also noted that when saltpeter is mixed with salt of ashes and then dissolved and evaporated the potash will precipitate first as squares and the saltpeter will appear last in needle form.[99]

Jorden suggested also that if the analyst did not wish to wait for the salts to crystallize they might be isolated in a second way, by precipitation

whereby those minerall substances are stricken downe from their concrete iuyces which held them, by addition of some opposite substance. And this is of two sorts: either Salts, as Tartar, Soape, Ashes, Kelps, Vrine, &c. Or sowre iuyces, as Vinegar, Lymons, Oyle of Vitrioll, Sulphur, &c. In which I have observed that the Salts are proper to blew colours, and the other to red: for example, take a piece of scarlet cloath, and wet it in Oyle of Tartar (the strongest of that kinde) and it presently becomes blew: dip it againe in Oyle of Vitriol, and it becomes red againe.[100]

This is an extremely early instance of the use of an acid-base indicator, for his Salts are all basic, while his "sowre iuyces" are acids. However, Jorden certainly was not consistent in his terms, for although all of his examples here are clear enough, in his other division of Salts into niter, alum, salt, and vitriol, such a definition would not hold. His observations with the scarlet cloth and crystallization are important, but Jorden failed to apply quantitative methods to his analyses—an approach which by the 1630s was not uncommon with other authors. Nevertheless, his work was quickly accepted as the most authoritative text on this subject in English and besides running to five editions it was frequently referred to by other authors.[101]

It is possible then to note an appreciable increase in knowledge from the tract of William Turner in 1557 to the manual of Edward Jorden sixty years later. The work of Fallopius and Gesner was made available in English in 1576 and this proved to be the most important of the Italian works on analysis. But this was a field which had been of great interest to the Paracelsians as well, and the influence of Thurneisser and Libavius became evident in the works of English authors not long afterwards. From the various treatises of the early seventeenth century it may be seen that the dissolved substances in mineral waters were isolated by evaporation, distillation, or precipitation. The residue was examined by taste, color, solubility, and its reaction on a red-hot coal. Further tests could be made on recrystallized samples of the salt through the identification of the crystalline shape of the substance. Finally, a few color indicators and color tests of other sorts were known to these men. Thus it was known that a scarlet-dyed cloth changed in color from red to blue when taken out of a "sowre iuyce" (acid) and dipped into a "salt" (base) solution. The juice of gall nuts was used as a test for alum, vitriol, or iron. At best this was a primitive approach to chemical analysis, but it was a great improvement over what had been known one hundred years earlier, and it does show that there had been a considerable amount of work in this field prior to the studies of Robert Boyle.

It is interesting also to note that the Paracelsians began to use the results of these analyses as a vindication for the use of chemical medicines at an early date. Thomas Tymme's 1605 translation from the works of Joseph Duchesne chides those who speak against metallic remedies as poisons with the fact that physicians universally sent their most hopeless cases to spas which contain "Niter, Allum, Vitriol, Sulphur, Pitch, Antimonie, Lead & such like: all which doe participate of a substance & spirit metallick".[102] Because of this there could be no question but that metallic medicines must also be beneficial to patients.

Also indicative of the growing interest in chemistry in this period was the application of chemical methods to geological problems by Gabriel Plattes.[103] This author strove to utilize man's new knowledge of nature for the benefit of mankind. Thus he wrote one work to encourage the improvement of agricultural practices,[104] while his second was written so that men might be able to identify valuable ores and minerals themselves. In the latter work it would seem that Plattes had been strongly influenced by William Gilbert, for he maintained that the earth was held in its central position in the universe by means of a magnetic attraction, equal in all directions, exerted on it by the celestial bodies.[105] With his interest in practical affairs he scorned the work of the alchemists,[106] although he believed that natural transmutations as well as artificial ones could occur. This, however, he dismissed as being unprofitable in his day since wages had risen to half a crown compared to the penny-a-day wages of several hundred years earlier.[107] Similarly Plattes believed in the value of the dowsing rod for finding deposits of valuable ores.[108] He was also interested in the relation of color to the analysis of substances, although he felt confident only in stating that blue crystals attest the presence of copper while white ones could mean any other metal.[109]

As a youth Plattes had believed that the rocks and mountains were not an original part of the earth and that they had grown with time like the warts and tumours on man.[110] However, he later changed his views and illustrated them with the following chemical experiment:

Let there bee had a great retort of Glasse, and let the same be halfe filled with Brimstone, Sea-coale, and as many bituminous and Sulphurious subterraneall substances as can bee gotten: then fill the necke thereof halfe full with the most free earth from stones that can be found, but thrust it not in too hard, then let it be luted, and set in an open Furnace to distill with a temperate Fire, which may onely kindle the said substances, and if you worke exquisitely, you shall finde the said earth petrified, and turned into a Stone: you shall also finde cracks and chinkes in it, filled with the most tenacious, clammy, and viscous parts of the said vapours, which ascended from the subterraneall combustible substances.[111]

Thus in nature, as in the retort, the rocks and mountains are formed from the vapors of bituminous and sulphureous substances while the veins of metals are engendered in the cracks and crannies of the mountains. Plattes went on to attribute the formation of hills and valleys to the action of the sea in former ages.[112]

With the exception of Plattes and a few metallurgists, Englishmen interested in chemistry in this period were medical men. They felt that it was important to analyze mineral waters in order to identify the valuable dissolved medicinal substances, and they turned to chemical methods because these seemed to give more definite answers than the simpler assessment by the senses. It was for practical reasons also that these men accepted chemically prepared medicines. There had been treatises on chemical medicines prior to any references to Paracelsus in England, and it was planned that the pharmacopoeia of 1585 should include a section on chemical medicines. But with the rapid spread of charlatans who styled themselves "Paracelsians", reputable medical authors carefully began to point out that there was a real difference between the true use and the abuse of chemistry in medicine. The Royal College of Physicians had no quarrel with sincere chemists, or even with some of the Paracelsians, but they strove energetically to stamp out all empirics who promoted one or two chemically prepared remedies and cloaked themselves with the title "Paracelsian".

The fact that sections on chemicals were included in the 1618 *Pharmacopoeia* is not of revolutionary importance in itself since it merely gave a formal recognition to the attitude taken by English physicians for the past thirty years. Nor was this acceptance of these remedies to be used as a springboard for further inroads on the traditional medicines. The chemical sections of this work remained practically unaltered for many successive editions and it was not until Nicholas Culpeper translated the *Pharmacopoeia* into English in 1649 that it was seen through his scathing marginal notations that there were some who felt that in this respect the official *Pharmacopoeia* was inadequate. Still, the average physician in 1640 felt much the same about chemical medicines as had his Elizabethan predecessor. Typical of them all was James Primerose who complained that Paracelsus was a magician who had tried to overturn Galenic medicine and replace it with his own. Such skullduggery was to be rejected by all true physicians, but this should not prejudice them against the use of chemistry in their practice. Indeed, "Physicians doe not dislike that chymicall preparation of remedies".—Why? Because for Primerose as well as for many others, chemical remedies did not originate with Paracelsus, but had been utilized "many ages before him, by Raimundus Lullius, Villanova, and many others . . . who, notwithstanding that, did professe the same art with the Galenists".[113]

Notes for Chapter Four

1. See Chapter 3. One of the best indications of the public attitude toward these alchemists may be found in Ben Jonson's satirical *Alchemist* (first presented 1610, 1st edition 1612).

2. John Baptista Lambye, *A Revelation of the Secret Spirit Declaring the Most concealed secret of Alchymie*, tr. R.N.E. gentleman (London, 1623), 74-80.

3. Arthur Dee, *Fasciculus Chemicus: or Chymical Collections*, tr. James Hasolle (Elias Ashmole) (London, 1650), sig. a 2. This work was first published in Latin at Paris in 1631.

4. Besides the Statutes themselves I have relied primarily on the following authorities for the account of the Royal College of Physicians during this period: C. R. B. Barrett, *The History of the Society of Apothecaries of London* (London, 1905); Dr. Charles Goodall, *The Royal College of Physicians of London* (London, 1684); O. M. Lloyd, "The Royal College of Physicians of London and Some City Livery Companies", *J. Hist. Med.*, *11* (1956), 412–21; Edward Kremers and George Urdang, *History of Pharmacy* (Philadelphia, 1951); and *Pharmacopoeia Londinensis of 1618 Reproduced in Facsimile with a Historical Introduction by George Urdang* (Madison, 1944). There was only one exception to the licensing power the Royal College exerted over physicians and surgeons in the London area in the sixteenth century. The same grant could be, and occasionally was, obtained from the Archbishop of Canterbury, but this practice gradually declined.

5. Lloyd, *loc. cit.*, 419.

6. *The Statutes at Large from the Thirty-second year of King Henry VIII to the Seventh Year of King Edward VI Inclusive*, ed. Danby Pickering (Cambridge, 1763), 32 Hen. VIII, c. 40, p. 57.

7. *The Statutes at Large from the First Year of Queen Mary to the Thirty-fifth year of Queen Elizabeth Inclusive*, ed. Danby Pickering (Cambridge, 1763), 1.Q.M. sessio secund., c. 9, p. 16. George Urdang concluded that the Paracelsian reforms reached England by 1553 because this act gave the Censors of the College the right "to survey and examine the stocks of apothecaries, druggists, distillers and sellers of waters and oils, and preparers of chemical medicines", Kremers and Urdang, *op. cit.*, 138; *Pharmacopoeia Londinensis . . . with a Historical Introduction by George Urdang*, 6. The mere reference to chemical medicines does not prove they were Paracelsian in origin. Beyond this, the text of the document does not refer to chemical medicines at all. As quoted by Pickering in the *Statutes at Large*, the act of 1553 merely gave the Censors the right to "search and view of Poticarye Wares Drugges and Compositions" (see also Goodall, *op. cit.*, 33). Kremers and Urdang seem to have obtained their quotation from the 1618 charter of the College which granted them the authority "to examine survey governe correct and punishe all and singular Physitians and practisers in the facultie of Physick Apothecaries Druggists Distillers and Sellers of waters or oyles Preparers of Chymical Medicynes . . ." (Goodall, *op. cit.*, 37).

8. *The Statutes at Large, From the Thirty-second Year of King Henry VIII to the Seventh Year of King Edward VI Inclusive*, ed. Danby Pickering (Cambridge, 1763), 35 Hen. VIII, c. 8, pp. 143–44. See also Kremers and Urdang, *op. cit.*, 138.

9. See above, p. 70.

10. Goodall, *op. cit.*, 364. Others prosecuted were surgeons such as William Foster and William Turner and even members of the clergy who dabbled in medicine. One of these was Henoch Clapham, a Nonconformist preacher who published a tract during the Plague of 1603 stating that a Christian who dies of the pest does so through a lack of faith; this naturally offended the ecclesiastical authorities. Then he also began to sell home-made medicines. As a result he

was prosecuted both by the College and by the Church. The latter saw to it that Clapham was sent to the Clink prison for three years. On Clapham see *ibid.*, 364, and the *DNB* article by Rev. Ronald Bayne (London, 1949–50) *4*, 371–72.

11. Goodall, *op. cit.*, 349–51.

12. Francis Anthony, *Medicinae Chymiae, et Veri Potabilis Auri assertio* (Cambridge, 1610), 25–31. On Anthony's life see *DNB*, *1*, 519–20. An article titled "The Contribution of Francis Anthony to Medicine" by George H. Evans (*Ann. Med. Hist.*, 3rd series, *2* (1940), 171–73) is an unfortunate eulogy.

13. Anthony, *Medicinae Chymiae*, 32.

14. *Collectanea Chymica* (London, 1684), 73–83. Anthony's process as described here consisted of three parts. After many repetitions of the basic process (heating "black tinne" and wine vinegar on a water bath, filtration and distillation) a final distillation gave the required "menstruum". While this was in process the operator was to prepare the "white calx of gold" from gold-dust and an aqueous salt solution. The gold calx and the menstruum were then supposedly reacted together by heating on a water bath. After discarding the supernatant liquor, the residue was extracted with alcohol. This "red" tincture was then distilled and the syrupy liquor remaining after the first fraction was removed was kept as the *aurum potabile*.

15. Matthew Gwinne, *In Assertorem Chymicae, sed Verae Medicinae Desertorem, Fra. Anthonium* (London, 1611). For Gwinne's life see the article by Norman Moore, M.D. in *DNB*, *8*, 842–43.

16. Gwinne, *op. cit.*, 109.

17. *Ibid.*, 21.

18. *Ibid.*, 22. "Non dico equidem chemiatros, Galeno-chymicos; è quibus esse pervelim, nec quin sin dubito: nec enim illi ista pollicentur, pollicendo pelliciunt in fraudem rerum imperitos."

19. Rawlin is not listed in *DNB*. For this information see Goodall, *op. cit.*, 347–48.

20. Thomas Rawlin, *A Warning to the False Chymists or The Philosophicall Alphabet* (British Museum Sloane Ms 3694, fols. 14–92), see fol. 15. Thomas Rawlin, *Admonitio Pseudo-Chymicis seu Alphabetarium Philosophicum* (London, *c.* 1610). See the "Candido et intelligenti Lectori".

21. Francis Anthony, *The Apologie, Or Defence of a Verity Heretofore Published concerning a Medicine Called Aurum Potabile* (London, 1616). Francis Anthony, *Apologia veritatis illucescentis pro auro potabile* (London, 1616).

22. John Cotta, *Cotta contra Antonium: or an Ant-Antony* (Oxford, 1623), 39, 53.

23. Robert Burton, *The Anatomy of Melancholy* (London, 1936), *2*, 240.

24. Helvig Dieterich, *Elogium Coelestium et Terrestrium, Macrocosmi & Microcosmi* (Argentorati, 1627). I have used the edition retitled *Novus Orbis* (Argentorati, 1631), 16.

25. Th. Brugis, *The Marrow of Physicke* . . . *A Medicamentory* (London, 1640), sig. b 3. Among his unguents he recommends "Stictick Paracelsus", Brugis, *Vade Mecum Or a Companion for a Chyrurgion* (London, 1651), 3.

26. *Ibid.*, 3, 105.

27. *Ibid.*, sig. b4.

28. A similar but less publicized case of this occurred in 1634 when John Evans, a minister, published a short tract praising the virtues of antimony as *The Universal Medicine*. He too quoted from the standard Paracelsian authors and argued that since antimony purifies gold, the noblest of metals, it would also purify the diseased human body. Evans held that by drinking from a cup made of antimony (which could be purchased from him for a slight consideration) all or most diseases could be cured. He even suggested that the cup be taken home and given a free trial before the actual purchase. Needless to say, he incurred the wrath of the College for much the same reason that Anthony had. His tract was ordered destroyed by the Archbishop of Canterbury and he was exposed as a quack trying to fleece the public by James Primerose, a member of the College, in 1640. For the proceedings against Evans see Goodall, *op. cit.*, 442–43. Also see James Primerose, Dr. of Physicke, *The Antimoniall Cup twice cast: Or, A Treatise concerning the Antimoniall Cup*, tr. Robert Wittie (London, 1640).

29. For a fuller description of this work see Kocher, *J. Hist. Med.*, *2* (1947), 466–67. For precise references to Paracelsus see John Banister, *An Antidotarie Chyrurgicall* (London, 1589), 20, 97–99, 103, 107, 135, 136, 296–97.

30. See Bredwell's introductory letter to Gerarde's *Herball* (1597) quoted in Chapter 2. This Stephen Bredwell (1597) was the father of the Stephen Bradwell of the 1630s.

31. Stephen Bradwell, *Helps for Suddain Accidents Endangering Life* (London, 1633), *Physick for the Sicknesse, Commonly Called the Plague* (London, 1636); also *A Watch-Man for the Pest* (London, 1625).

32. The Harper reprint of Hester's *Keys of Philosophy* was retitled *A Storehouse of Physicall and Philosophicall Secrets Teaching to distill all manner of Oyles from Gummes, Spices, Seedes, Rootes, Hearbs, and Mineralls, &c.*

33. John Wood, *Practicae Medicinae liber, vocatus Amalgama* (London, 1596), 21.

34. Thomas Bonham, *The Chyrurgians Closet* (London, 1630), sig. A2. Among the authorities cited in this volume are John Banister, Arnold of Villanova, George Baker, William Clowes, Valerius Cordus, Isabella Cortese, Gesner, Fioravanti, Thomas Gale, William Gilbert, Paracelsus, Paré, Quercetanus, Ruland, Vesalius, and Thurneisser.

35. Little is known of Hart's life. On this see *DNB*, *9*, 60. He studied at Paris and in Germany, graduated abroad, and practiced at Northampton.

36. James Hart, *KΛINIKH, or The Diet of the Diseased* (London, 1633), fol. Ooo 2. See also his views on the danger of Paracelsian remedies in his *Anatomy of Urines* (London, 1625), 126.

37. Hart, *KΛINIKH*, 354–72.

38. *Ibid.*, 372.

39. *Ibid.*, 6.

40. Henry Cuffe, *The Differences of the Ages of Mans Life* (London, 1607), 71–72.

41. Sir William Vaughn, *The Newlanders Cure* (London, 1630), 44–45.

42. Angelus Sala, *Opiologia or, A Treatise concerning the Nature, properties, true*

preparation and safe use and administration of Opium, tr. and enlarged by Tho. Bretnor M.M. (London, 1618), Preface.

43. *Ibid.*, Preface sigs. B–B6.
44. John Cotta, *A Short Discoverie of the Unobserved Dangers of severall sorts of ignorant and inconsiderate Practisers of Physicke in England* (London, 1612), 82.
45. Burton, *op. cit.*, 240f.
46. Leslie G. Matthews, *History of Pharmacy in Britain* (Edinburgh and London, 1962), 73.
47. For a discussion of this in more detail see George Urdang, "How Chemicals Entered the Official Pharmacopoeias", *Arch. Int. Hist. Sci.*, *33* (1954), 304–13. See also Urdang's historical introduction to his reprint of the first 1618 edition of the London *Pharmacopoeia*.
48. Urdang, *Arch. Int. Hist. Sci.*, *33*, 305–06.
49. See Chapter 2 and Urdang, *Pharmacopoeia Londinensis 1618*, 11.
50. For two good brief accounts of this see Lynn Thorndike, *History of Magic and Experimental Science*, 6, 247–48, and Dr. A. G. Chevalier, "The Antimony War—A Dispute Between Montpellier and Paris", *Ciba Symposia*, *2* (1940), 418–23.
51. On Mayerne's life see Thomas Gibson, "A Sketch of the Career of Theodore Turquet de Mayerne", *Ann. Med. Hist.*, New Series, *5* (1933), 315–26. This is not always sound, but it is the best biography available.
52. Urdang, *Pharm. Lond. 1618*, 20.
53. Barrett, *op. cit.*, xvi.
54. *Pharmacopoeia Londinensis* (2nd edition, London, 1618), "Candido Lectori".
55. Urdang, *Pharm. Lond. 1618*, 64–72. See also Urdang, *Arch. Int. Hist. Sci.*, *33* (1954), 310–13. Besides Atkins and Mayerne, other members who were listed as living members at the time of publication were the following physicians whose works we have considered: Edward Jorden, Francis Herring, Matthew Gwinne, William Harvey, and Robert Fludd.

The May edition of 1618 had given full titles to some of the members of the College while neglecting to do this for others. Further, some of the preparations had been specifically ascribed to certain members. Urdang has suggested in the above-cited works that this aroused enough professional jealousy to enable the slighted members to have the first edition recalled.

56. This rough count of the number of articles in the different editions may be compared with the study of Dietrich Arends and Wolfgang Schneider on the drugs which received official sanction in Brunswick in the sixteenth and seventeenth centuries (*Die Braunschweiger Apothekenregister 1506–1673* (Braunschweig, 1960), as summarized in Schneider, "Der Wandel des Arzneischatzes im 17. Jahrhundert und Paracelsus", *Sudhoffs Archiv*, *45* (1961), 203 ff.). While the number of listed drugs increased from 1200 to 2800 in the century 1566–1666, the traditional herbal remedies dropped off from 33% to 26% of the total. Similarly the old-fashioned polypharmaceuticals dropped off from 32% to 22%. At the same time all chemically altered drugs increased their percentages—the most spectacular increase being made by the

inorganic remedies, which composed only 2% of the total in 1566 and rose to 7·5% a hundred years later. Schneider argues therefore that the shift to chemical remedies was slow but appreciable during the chemiatric period. Further basic changes in the pharmacopoeia do not occur until after 1800.

57. Urdang, *Pharm. Lond. 1618*, 51.

58. *Ibid.*, 72.

59. According to his manuscript notes, Mayerne took this out of Hester's translation of the "Spagerical preparations" of Quercetanus. *Pharmacopoeia Londinensis* (2nd edition, London, 1618—British Museum copy with Mayerne's notes), 180.

60. D. Gordon, *Pharmaco-Pinax* (Aberdeen, 1625).

61. *Ibid.*, 7.

62. *Ibid.*, 36–40.

63. Brice Bauderon, *Pharmacopoea*, tr. into Latin by Philemon Holland (London, 1639), 261, 266–67.

64. Goodall, *op. cit.*, 44.

65. On this see the Company of Distillers of London, *The Distiller of London* (London, 1639), 5–11. See also Lloyd, *loc. cit.*, 415; Barrett, *op. cit.*, 8–57 *passim*.

66. Pagel, *Paracelsus*, 189–200.

67. R. B., *op. cit.*, sig. Evii.

68. John Cotta, *A Short Discoverie etc.*, 103–11. James Primerose, *Popular Errours Or the Errours of the People in Physick*, tr. Robert Wittie (London, 1651), 56–59; this work was published first in Latin in 1638. Thomas Brian, M.P., *The Pisse-Prophet Or Certaine Pisse-Pot Lectures* (London, 1637). Brian had practised in London, and was residing in Colchester when he wrote this work.

69. For a lucid analysis of Hart's contribution in this field see Pagel, *Paracelsus*, 196–98. Hart's work on urinalysis is best set out in his *The Anatomie of Urine* (London, 1625) where he discusses the Paracelsian approach to this problem on pp. 119–21. However, he had in 1623 translated a similar work by Peter Forrest titled *The Arraignment of Urines*. In his preface to this latter work he also attacks the chemical analysis of urine (see sig. A2).

70. See the present author's paper, "Solution Analyses prior to Robert Boyle", *Chymia, 8* (1962), 41–61.

71. Giacomo de Dondi, *Tractatus de causa salsedinis aquarum, & modo conficiendi salis ex eis, De Balneis omnia quae extant apud Graecos, Latinos et Arabas* (Venice, 1553), fol. 109.

72. Johannes Michael Savonarola, *De balneis et termis naturalibus omnibus ytalie* (Ferrara, 10 November 1485), fol. 26, Chapter 27.

73. Paracelsus, "Eilff Tractat oder Bücher vom Ursprung und ursacher", *Opera: Bücher und Schriften*, ed. J. Huser (2 vols., Strassburg, 1616), *1*, 521.

74. Georgius Agricola, *De natura corum quae effluunt ex terra. Libri IV.* (1545), in *Ausgewählte Werke*, ed. Hans Prescher (7 vols., Berlin, 1955–63), *1*, 213–319.

75. The edition I have used is Gabrielis Falloppii Mutinensis, *De Medicatis Aquis atque de Fossilibus* (Venice, 1569), fols. 30–37.

76. On the work of Paracelsus in mineral water analyses see Gernot Rath, "Die Anfägne der Mineralquellenanalyse", *Medizinischen Monatsschrift*, *3* (1949), 539–41.

77. Leonhart Thurneisser zum Thurn, *Pison* (Frankfort on the Oder, 1572), 31–38, 43–46. Andreas Libavius, "De Iudicio Aquarum Mineralium et horum quae cum illis inveniuntur", *Alchemia* (Frankfort, 1597), 275–392.

78. William Turner, Dean of Wells, *A Booke of the natures and properties as well of the bathes in England as of other bathes in Germanye and Italye* (Collen, 1568; 1st ed., Collen, 1562). Preface dated March 10, 1557, at Basle. The Savonarola quote may be found on fol. 7. For Turner's work as a naturalist see Charles E. Raven, *English Naturalists from Neckham To Ray* (Cambridge, 1947), 48–137.

79. Turner, *op. cit.*, fol. 1.

80. Conrad Gesner, *The Newe Iewell of Health*, tr. Thomas Hill, corrected and published in English by George Baker (London, 1576), fols. 41–44.

81. Walter Bailey, *A Briefe Discours of certain Bathes of medicinall Waters in the Countie of Warwicke neere unto a village called Newnam Regis* (London, 1587), 10–13. Bailey is perhaps known best for his *A Briefe treatise touching the preservation of the eiesight* (London, 1586). I have used the 1626 edition of this work which is annexed to Sir W. Vaughn's *Directions for health.*

82. Robert Wittie, *Scarbrough-Spaw: or a Description of the Nature and Vertues of the Spaw at Scarbrough Yorkshire* (York, 1667), 5.

83. Edmund Deane, *Spadacrene Anglica or The English Spaw-Fountaine* (London, 1626), 12.

84. *Ibid.*, 6; Michael Stanhope, *Newes out of York-Shire: Or, An Account of a Iourney in the True Discovery of a Souveraigne Minerall, Medicinall Water* (London, 1626), and *Cures Without Care, or a Summons to all Such Who Finde Little or no helpe by the use of ordinary physick to repaire to the Northerne Spaw* (London, 1632), 6.

85. Libavius, *op. cit.*, sig. c.

86. Edward Jorden, *A Briefe Discourse of a Disease Called the Suffocation of the Mother* (London, 1603).

87. Edward Jorden, *A Discourse of Naturall Bathes, and Minerall Waters* (London, 1631), 35. Four other editions of this work were printed, in 1632, 1633, 1669, and 1673.

88. *Ibid.* (1632 edition), 96.

89. *Ibid.* (1631 edition), 73.

90. *Ibid.* (1632 edition), 91.

91. *Ibid.*, 74–78.

92. *Ibid.* (1631 edition), 5.

93. *Ibid.*, 73–76.

94. *Ibid.*, 9.

95. *Ibid.*, 17–76.

96. *Ibid.*, 29.

97. *Ibid.*, 76.

98. *Ibid.* (1632 edition), 38.

99. *Ibid.*, 38. It would appear that Jorden is in error here, for from the solubilities of K_2CO_3 and KNO_3 one might expect the saltpeter to precipitate first. Indeed, in a description of a similar process, Nicolas Lemery concludes that "the long crystals that we see Salt-peter shoot into, do proceed from its volatile part, for that which is crystallized last, is fixt like sea-salt, and looks just like it". Nicolas Lemery, *A Course of Chymistry*, tr. Walter Harris M.D. (2nd edition from the 5th French edition, London, 1686), 292.

100. Jorden (1631 edition), 76. One cannot be certain just what dye was in the cloth Jorden used—however, in a letter to the author Sidney M. Edelstein has pointed out that the common scarlet dye in Jorden's lifetime was cochineal or kermes and that these "would have acted exactly as Jorden describes the reactions with alkali and acid in his test".

101. Although complaining of the difficulty of determining the contents of springs. Rowzee (1632) referred his readers to Jorden on this problem. Lodowick Rowzee, *The Queenes Wells* (London, 1632), 28, 33–34. Again, Thomas Johnson suggested that the reader should turn to Jorden to learn of the minerals in the Bath waters. Thomas Johnson, *Thermae Bathonicae* (London, 1634), 6. Similarly in 1652 and 1660 John French and Robert Wittie felt it necessary to refute in considerable detail Jorden's views on the origin of hot springs. John French, *The York-shire Spaw* (London, 1652), 10–11; Robert Wittie, *Scarbrough-Spaw* (London, 1660), 91 ff.

102. Joseph Duchesne (Quercetanus), *The Practise of Chymicall, and Hermeticall Physicke*, sig. Q3 (v).

103. Practically nothing is known of Plattes' life. He had had relatively little formal education, but he had become obsessed with the need to utilize the knowledge of nature for the benefit of mankind—a thoroughly Baconian viewpoint. In this he was warmly encouraged by his friend Samuel Hartlib. He is supposed to have died destitute during the period of the Commonwealth. See *DNB*, 15, 1296, and also the author's paper "Gabriel Plattes and his Chemical theory of the Formation of the Earth's Crust", *Ambix*, 9 (1961), 162–65.

104. Gabriel Plattes, *A Discovery of Infinite Treasure* (London, 1639).

105. *Ibid.*, 1–2.

106. *Ibid.*, sig. a.

107. Gabriel Plattes, *A Discovery of Subterraneall Treasure* (London, 1639), 40–43. Plattes believed he had transmuted regulus of iron and copper to gold and he gave his procedure to the reader at this point.

108. *Ibid.*, 11–13.

109. *Ibid.*, 9–10.

110. *Ibid.*, 5.

111. *Ibid.*, 6.

112. *Ibid.*, 6–8.

113. Primerose, *Popular Errours*, 34.

Chapter Five

Epilogue

THE eighty-year period from the first mention of Paracelsus in an English book (by William Turner, 1557) to the death of Robert Fludd (1637) may be treated as a whole. Although important advances had been made in all fields of science during these crucial years of the Scientific Revolution, the problems connected with the acceptance or rejection of Paracelsism remained much the same in the 1630s as they had in the last quarter of the previous century.

A definite compromise had been reached in England in regard to this new medicine: the occult aspects of Paracelsian thought were rejected while the new remedies were eagerly adopted, provided they proved their worth. This had been the compromise position set forth by William Clowes and most other surgeons at the end of the sixteenth century. It was the opinion also of many physicians. Stephen Bredwell, for instance, fought the "pernicious impostures and sophistications" of the Paracelsians, but at the same time wanted to establish a chemical lectureship at the Royal College of Physicians (1597).[1] This attitude remained unaltered in the new century, and it could just as easily have been Bredwell writing forty years earlier when James Primerose stated (1638) that

. . . though the Galenists doe justly refuse the doctrine of Paracelsus, yet they do not dissallow of chymicall remedies, but leave them their own place in Physick. And the Chymists themselves cannot be without

175

remedies prepared after the vulgar way, as is evident in Quercetanus, and others, yea and Paracelsus himself, who prescribes many decoctions and infusions, and uses many things whole not changed at all by any chymicall art. Therefore to both of them their own praise is due; for sometimes there is need of using chymicall remedies, sometimes, yea, very often, the other.[2]

As a result, the role played by Paracelsus in the Renaissance transformation of pharmacy was ignored by most Elizabethans and Paracelsus was at best listed as one of many who approved of these remedies.

Chemical therapy had won acceptance in England not by overturning the Galenic system, but by allying itself to it. On the Continent the conservatives who had been shocked at the desire of Paracelsus to discard the whole ancient medical corpus had begun to band together as a faction shortly after 1550. There were two clearly defined groups, the one wishing to discard much of the old medicine, the other in defense clearly being forced to adhere to its authorities rigidly. When Conrad Gesner, who was only eleven in 1527 when Paracelsus burned the *Canon* of Avicenna, later compiled a group of chemical remedies from various authors, his production was not to cause any widespread controversy. This work was still in the tradition of the medieval medical alchemists who had no real quarrel with the Galenists.

But in England the course of events was somewhat different. Apart from the translation of Brunschwig's work on distillation which had appeared in 1527, and the translation of one of Arnold of Villanova's works (1540), the first volume of chemical remedies, both organic and inorganic, was the *Treasure of Euonymus* of Gesner (1559). This was not a theoretical work, but it did make available a great number of useful remedies. Most important was the fact that although the author had no recourse to Galen or Hippocrates in its compilation, he sought no quarrel with them. In the 1560s and the 1570s the English physicians had no reason to believe that these remedies implied any conflict with the existing system. When the first comments on Paracelsus and the Paracelsian theories were printed in England in the monographs of John Jones and George Baker in the seventies, they were based not on the works of Paracelsus himself, but rather on the refutation of his theories by Thomas Erastus. And when R. Bostocke tried in 1585 to present a more accurate summary of the Paracelsian system his work attracted very little interest. The other outstanding Paracelsian treatise of this period by an Englishman was the 1584 tract by Thomas Moffett, but although he appears to have read widely in the Paracelsian corpus, his purpose was primarily to aid in the acceptance of the new medicines. In any case, his work was never printed in England and it seems to have attracted little attention there, although his views were no doubt known to his colleagues in the Royal College of Physicians.

The rest of the chief supporters of the new medicine in England were interested less in theory than in practice, and thus John Hester and the members of the Barber-Surgeons' Company can be placed in the Gesnerian rather than in the Paracelsian tradition. While on the Continent a physician was often in a position where he could choose only between an almost complete overthrow and an equally complete dominance of the Galenic medicine, in England the physician generally chose to accept the Galenic system with the addition of whatever was found valuable in chemical therapy. It was this solution which found almost immediate acceptance even in the supposedly conservative Royal College of Physicians.

The more complete expositions of Paracelsian thought which became available with the Duchesne translation by Thomas Tymme in 1605 and Tymme's own defense in 1612, as well as with the Fluddean system of the world which began to be published in 1617, did nothing to reverse this trend. The influence of Duchesne's views on the elements may be traced through a series of early seventeenth-century works, but few English authors were interested in this subject. Robert Fludd was England's most important mystical alchemist. His many folio volumes discussing his philosophy give us valuable insight into the neo-Platonic and Paracelsian approach to nature in this period. His universe was filled with angels and demons and he spoke with sincerity of magic and demoniacal rites. Yet to him, as to many Paracelsians, it was right and proper to investigate nature by means of observation and experiment in order to understand more fully the goodness of God to man. As an extreme proponent of mystical alchemy, Fludd alarmed Continental investigators such as Kepler, Mersenne, and Gassendi, whose approach to nature would today be considered more sound. But we have seen that Thomas Tymme had argued for experimental investigations because God had given man two books to read—the Bible and the book of nature.[3] Fludd also argued from experimental evidence when he so desired, as may be seen in his correct refutation of Gassendi in their dispute over the existence of the pores in the intraventricular septum. Similarly Thomas Moffett, in affirming the elemental nature of the three principles, referred to the analytical observations of chemists rather than tradition.[4] But in spite of this experimental approach, the work of Fludd and the other early seventeenth-century English alchemists attained no popularity in England. It was on the Continent that Fludd became famous, and especially in Germany, where the Paracelsian and the alchemical traditions were much stronger than in England. At home he was accused of witchcraft, while abroad his works were published in sumptuous editions.

The English lack of interest in Fludd's works is in keeping with the Elizabethan rejection of Paracelsian theory. On the other hand, the early and favorable view toward chemically prepared remedies was maintained in the new century. Chemical remedies had been accepted very early by the Elizabethan surgeons and also by many of the physicians, and that the Royal College of Physicians was not hostile to the new medicines is evidenced by the section on chemical medicines planned for their proposed pharmacopoeia of 1585. The *Pharmacopoeia* of

1618 also belongs to this Elizabethan spirit of compromise; here reliance was placed primarily on the traditional remedies, but the chemical oils, balsams, and wound plasters were granted an auxiliary role. Only gradually was the close relationship of Paracelsus with the new medicines generally admitted. In 1635 Alexander Read, a Galenist lecturer at Barber-Surgeons' Hall, felt it necessary to explain Paracelsian as well as traditional medicine to his students,[5] and by this time chemical remedies were often considered Paracelsian in origin whether or not this was actually true.

A second major application of chemistry and chemical methods during this period was in the analysis of mineral waters. As with chemically prepared remedies, the origins of this analysis date back to the late middle ages, but again considerable impetus was given it by the late sixteenth-century Paracelsians. It is possible to follow the development of solution analysis in the writings of the English analysts, from the crude description of William Turner (1557) to the remarkable work of Edward Jorden (1631) which reflects and in some respects surpasses the analytical procedure of his better known friend, Andreas Libavius. By the time of Jorden many of the basic methods of qualitative analysis were already in use, among them color indicators and flame tests, specific gravity determinations, and the use of crystal forms as a means of identification. As with chemical therapy, the chemical analysis of aqueous solutions gained currency because of practical considerations—in this case due to its obvious improvement over the earlier method of checking a water simply by its appearance and taste. The information gained from these new methods of analysis was quickly applied in defense of the chemists' inorganic medicines.

This was the age of iatrochemistry: to the Paracelsian and the Galenist alike chemistry had no other purpose than to aid the physician. The question was: how great was the place of chemistry in medicine? To the Paracelsian theorist the universe could be explained in alchemical terms from the divine Creation to the present. R. Bostocke in 1585 felt that true "phisicke" was nothing but chemistry or alchemy and that it could be defined as the search for the secrets of nature.[6] But because of the interrelation of all parts of nature, the microcosm as well as the macrocosm must be founded on chemical processes. Illnesses were interpreted as internal chemical disorders, the physiology of the body was ruled by the Archeus in the stomach which acted the role of an internal alchemist, and the blood circulated through the body in much the same fashion as in the chemists' distillations. In short, the body itself was thought of as a large piece of chemical equipment. Typical of this whole attitude is the following (rather late) description of the common cold given by Thomas Willis:

the Brain with a Scull over it, and the appending Nerves, represent the little Head or Glassie Alembic, with a Spunge laid upon it, as we use to do for the highly rectifying of the Spirit of Wine: for truly the Blood when rarified by Heat, is carried from the Chimny of the Heart, to the Head even as the Spirit of Wine boyling in the Cucurbit, and being resolved into Vapour, is elevated into the Alembic; where the Spunge covering all the opening of the Hole, only transmits or suffers to pass through the more penetrating and very subtil Spirits, and carried them to the snout of the Alembic. . . .[7]

And so he goes on describing physiological processes in such simple chemical terms. But relatively few physicians in England approved of the occult theories of the iatrochemists, and for the most part they limited the scope of chemistry to the preparation of medicines. This was the view of the pharmacists, the surgeons, and many members of the Royal College of Physicians. These men, ignoring the mystical alchemical associations which they made no pretense of understanding, would have agreed with James Primerose (1638) when he wrote that

Chymistry is not an art of its own kinde, but meerly a preparation of medicaments, and therefore in proper speaking belongs to that part of Physick called Pharmacie, and so ought not to be treated but in Pharmacie.[8]

For such men an extension of this definition could only be made for some equally practical purpose such as the analytical usages we have described.

Paracelsus and his theoretical reforms became very unpopular, even before they were properly explained, and the view toward them which was taken in the first ten years after their introduction in England was basically the same as expressed in the *Pharmacopoeia* of 1618. The chief Elizabethan translator of works on spagirical medicine had been John Hester, and it is significant that he was far more interested in the recipe books of Duchesne and Fioravanti than in Paracelsus. His two short translations from works falsely attributed to Paracelsus were composed of chemical recipes, not of iatrochemical theory, and even more important is the fact that they were the only translations attributed to Paracelsus until the 1650s.

During the forties and the fifties a host of new ideas and systems of thought were to affect English Paracelsism to a greater or lesser degree. The revival of atomism, the introduction of Cartesian thought, and the growing influence of the Baconian writings all affected the philosophical views of this period. Most important to the English Paracelsians after 1640 was the publication of the works of J. B. van Helmont (1577–1644) whose collected writings first appeared in 1648. Translations of some of them began to appear in English as early as 1650. These had such a profound effect on the English Paracelsians that during the fifties the physicians who subscribed to these views were frequently referred to as "Paracelso-Helmontians". Helmont's work brought a new interest to the Paracelsian corpus, and the conflict which developed at that time was far more violent than that which had led to the Elizabethan compromise in medicine. It resulted in the translation of many more works of Paracelsus plus a reprint of the Hester translations. The chemists, becoming ever more partisan, began to take sharp issue with the College of Physicians and others who had been brought up in the spirit of the Elizabethan compromise. For

George Starkey, George Thomson, and the other "chemical physicians" of London it was not enough to accept only some of the chemically prepared medicines; they called for the replacement of the Galenic corpus with a medicine based on chemistry. Previously there had been no assault on the official *Pharmacopoeia* which reflected the interest of the London physicians in chemistry; but in 1649 Nicholas Culpeper, in the notations to his translation of the then current edition, scathingly attacked the College for its views on chemical remedies. Thus, in preparing the section on "Chemical Oyls and other Liquors", Culpeper faithfully translated the directions of the Latin edition and then went on to advise the reader that

> Your best way to learn to still Chymical Oyls, is to learn of an Alchymist: for I rest confident the greatest part of the Colledg had no more skil in Chemistry, than I have in building houses; but having found out certain Models in old rusty Authors, tell people SO they must be done.[9]

In a similar vein, Noah Biggs in 1651 complained of the Galenical basis of English medicine and said that instead it should be based on experimental chemistry. Biggs accused the Galenists of an "antipathy" to the Commonwealth, and he demanded that the College of Physicians should be reformed.[10]

As the decade of the fifties progressed, this split between the new Paracelso-Helmontians and the College increased in intensity. Prominent chemists like George Starkey and George Tonstal challenged the Galenists to public trials of the effectiveness of the two systems.[11] But the Paracelsian theorists suffered a damaging blow with the brilliant attack on the three principles made by Robert Boyle in his *Sceptical Chymist* (1661), while those chemical physicians who had discarded most of the Galenist heritage were also discredited by their failure to halt the Plague in London in 1665.[12] As a result this new controversy led to a reconfirmation of the stand first taken by the Elizabethans. The views of the extreme Paracelsian iatrochemists were once more rejected and the road was open for Robert Boyle and his contemporaries to extend the goals of chemistry beyond the views of the pharmacists and the chemical physicians and at the same time to base this science on newer philosophical systems.

Notes for Chapter Five

1. John Gerarde, *The Herball or Generall Historie of Plantes* (London, 1597), introductory non-paginated leaf titled "To the well affected Reader and peruser of this book" by Stephen Bredwell.
2. James Primerose, *Popular Errours Or the Errours of the People in Physick*, tr. Robert Wittie (London, 1651), 222–23. This work was published first in Latin in 1638.
3. Thomas Tymme, *A Dialogue Philosophicall* (London, 1612). From the dedication to Sir Edward Coke, Lord Chief Justice of the Court of Common Pleas, sig. A3.
4. Thomas Moffett, "De Jure et Praestantia Chemicorum Medicamentorum", *Theatrum Chemicum*, ed. L. Zetzner (Argentorati, 1659), *1*, 100.
5. Alexander Read, *The Chirurgicall Lectures of Tumors and Ulcers* (London, 1635), 3–4, 24–25, 101–02. Read (Reid, or Rhaedus) (1586?–1641) was an anatomist and surgeon educated at Aberdeen University who later studied surgery in France. In 1632 he was appointed lecturer on anatomy at Barber-Surgeons' Hall. See *DNB* article by D'Arcy Power (1921–22 ed., *16*, 867–69).
6. R.B. esq., *The difference betwene the auncient Phisicke . . . and the latter Phisicke* (London, 1585), sig. Bi (r).
7. Thomas Willis, *Of Fermentation* (1st Latin edition—1659). See the translation by S. Pordage in Willis' *Practise of Physick* (London, 1684), 12–13.
8. Primerose, *op. cit.*, 222–23.
9. I have consulted Culpeper's translation of the second edition of the *Pharmacopoeia*: Nicholas Culpeper, *Pharmacopoeia Londinensis: or the London Dispensatory . . .* (6th ed., London, 1659), 328.
10. Noah Biggs, *Mataeotechnia Medicinae Praxeωs* (London, 1651), sig. b1, p. 3
11. George Starkey, *Natures Explication and Helmont's Vindication* (London, 1651); see the "Epistle Dedicatory". On Tonstall's challenge, see Robert Wittie's remarks in his *Scarborough Spagirical Anatomiser dissected* (1672). This work is abstracted in Thomas Short, M.D., *The Natural, Experimental, and Medicinal History of the Mineral Waters of Derbyshire, Lincolnshire, and Yorkshire* (London, 1734), 143–48. Wittie himself was similarly challenged. See F. N. L. Poynter, "A Seventeenth-Century Medical Controversy: Robert Witty versus William Simpson", *Science, Medicine and History. Essays in honour of Charles Singer* (2 vols., London, 1953), *2*, 72–81.
12. Sir Henry Thomas, "The Society of Chymical Physitians, an echo of the Great Plague of London", *ibid.*, 56–71.

Bibliography

The English primary sources listed below I located with the aid of A. W. Pollard and G. R. Redgrave, *A Short Title Catalogue of Books Printed in England, Scotland & Ireland* . . . *1475–1640* (London, 1926) which I scanned for titles of possible chemical or medical interest. However, since this is a study of the English Paracelsians rather than of works printed in England, I also searched for the Continental publications of English authors through the catalogues of the major European libraries. Additional titles I obtained through the references made by these English authors to Continental works they had used.

In my search for copies of these books, the rich holdings of Houghton and Widener Libraries at Harvard University were of inestimable value; Houghton Library in particular has very strong holdings of sixteenth-century English medical works. Also in the Cambridge area is the Boston Medical Library, to whose remarkable collection of early medical volumes I often referred. During the year 1959–60 I continued my research in England at the Cambridge University Library, the Wellcome Historical Medical Library, and the British Museum, where I was able to complete my examination of all but perhaps a dozen of the works listed in the *Short Title Catalogue* which seemed to be of interest. Although I examined a few manuscripts, most of my attention was directed to the printed sources, since few of these had been studied previously in regard to their Paracelsian content.

The Bibliography has been arranged under the following headings:

1. *Primary Sources.*

  A. Paracelsus—a listing of the various editions of the works of Paracelsus consulted.
  B. Relevant works of other authors.

2. *Secondary Sources.*

3. *Dictionaries, and Biographical and Bibliographical aids.*

184

1. PRIMARY SOURCES

A. PARACELSUS

Paracelsus. *Chirurgische Bücher und Schrifften.* Edited by J. Huser. Strassburg, 1618.

Paracelsus. *Four Treatises of Theophrastus von Hohenheim called Paracelsus.* Translated from the original German, with introductory essays by C. Lilian Temkin, George Rosen, Gregory Zilboorg, and Henry E. Sigerist. Edited with a preface by Henry E. Sigerist, Baltimore, 1941.

Paracelsus. *The Hermetic and Alchemical Writings of Paracelsus.* Translated and edited by A. E. Waite. 2 vols. London, 1894.

Paracelsus. *The occult causes of disease. Being a compendium of the teachings laid down in his "Volumen Paramirum" by Bombastus von Hohenheim, better known as Paracelsus.* Translated by Agnes Blake. London, 1930.

Paracelsus. *Of the Supreme Mysteries of Nature.* Translated by R. Turner. London, 1655.

Paracelsus. *Opera Bücher und Schrifften.* Edited by J. Huser. 2 vols. Strassburg, 1616.

Paracelsus. *Selected Writings.* Edited with an introduction by Jolande Jacobi, translated by Norbert Guterman. New York, 1951.

Paracelsus. *Sieben Defensionem.* Cologne, 1564. Reprinted by H. E. Sigerist. Leipzig, 1928.

Paracelsus. *Volumen Medicinae Paramirum.* Translated by K. F. Leidecker. *Supplement to the Bulletin of the History of Medicine,* No. 11. Baltimore, 1949.

Theophrast von Hohenheim genannt Paracelsus. *Sämtliche Werke.* Edited by Karl Sudhoff and Wilhelm Matthiessen. 15 vols. Munich and Berlin, 1922–33.

The editions of Huser and of Sudhoff and Matthiessen have been of most use to the author.

B. RELEVANT WORKS OF OTHER AUTHORS

Abraham, M. Nicolas. *Description de la Fontaine Minerale, depuis peu Descouverte Au Terroir de Reims en Champagne.* Paris, 1606.

Agricola, Georgius. *Ausgewählte Werke,* ed. Hans Prescher (7 vols., Berlin, 1955–63).

Agricola, Georgius. *De Re Metallica.* Translated by Herbert C. Hoover and Lou Henry Hoover. London, 1912.

Agrippa, Henry Corn. *Of the vanitie and uncertaintie of artes and sciences.* Translated by Ja. Sanford. London, 1569.

Albertus Magnus. *The boke of secretes.* London, n.d.

Albertus Magnus. *Secretes of the vertues of herbes.* London, 1549.

Alexis of Piedmont. *The secretes of the reverende Maister Alexis of Piedmont.* 4 parts. London, 1562, 1563, 1562, 1569.

Andernach, Johann Winter von. *Commentarius de Balneis et aquis medicatis in tres Dialogos distinctus.* Argentorati, 1565.

Anthony, Francis. *Apologia veritatis illucescentis pro auro potabile.* London, 1616.

Anthony, Francis. *The Apologie, or, defence of a verity heretofore published concerning a medicine called Aurum Potabile.* London, 1616.

Anthony, Francis. "'Aurum Potabile,' or the receipt of Dr. F. A. shewing his way and method, how he made and prepared that most excellent medicine for the body of man", in *Collectanea Chymica.* London, 1684.

Anthony, Francis. *Medicinae Chymicae, et Veri Potabilis Auri assertio.* Cambridge, 1610.

Antidotharius, The. *The Antidotharius, in the whiche thou mayst lerne howe thou shalte make many and dyvers noble playsters, salves, oyntementes, powders, bawmes, oyles and wounde drynkes. . . .* London, 1530.

Arceus, Franciscus. *A most excellent and Compendious Method of curing woundes in the head.* Translated by John Read. London, 1588.

Arnaldus de Villanova. *Here is a newe boke, called the defence of age and recovery of youth.* Translated by J. Drummond. London, 1540.

Askham, Anthony. *A litell treatyse of astronomy, very necessary for physyke and surgerye, declarynge what herbes, and all kynde of medecynes are appropryate and under the influence of the planetes.* London, 1552.

Baccius, Andrea. *De Thermis.* (1st ed. 1571.) Venice, 1588.

Bacon, Roger. *Opera Quaedam Hactenus Inedita.* Edited by J. S. Brewer. London, 1859.

Bacon, Roger. *The Opus Majus.* Translated by R. B. Burke. Philadelphia, 1928.

Bacon, Roger. *This Boke doth treate all of the best waters Artyfycialles. . . .* London (1530?).

Bailey, Walter. *A Briefe Discours of certain bathes or medicinall Waters in the Countie of Warwicke neere unto a village called Newnam Regis.* London, 1587.

Bailey, Walter. *A briefe treatise touching the preservation of the eiesight.* London, 1586. A new edition (London, 1626) added to Sir W. Vaughn's *Directions for health.*

Baker, George. *The Composition or making of the moste excellent and pretious oil called Oleum Magistrale. . . .* London, 1574.

Balneis omnia quas extant apud Graecos, De, Latinos et Arabas. Venice, 1553.

Banister, John. *An Antidotarie Chyrurgicall*. London, 1589.

Banister, John. *The Historie of Man, sukked from the sappe of the most approved Anathomistes in this present Age*. London, 1578.

Banister, John. *A Needefull, new, and necessarie treatise of Chyrurgerie*. London, 1575.

Banister, John. *The Workes of that famous Chyrurgian. . . . To which is added a Treatise for distilling of Oyles of all sorts, with a perfect order to prepare all Minerals, and to draw forth their Oyles and Salts, &c.* 3 vols. London, 1633.

Barrough, Philip. *The Method of Phisicke*. 6th ed. London, 1624.

Bartholomaeus, Anglicus. *Batman uppon Bartholome, his booke. De Proprietatibus rerum*, enlarged and amended. London, 1582.

Batman, Stephen. *A booke of ye coppies of letters, Libells, & Other Inventions of Men*. [*c.* 1582]. Houghton manuscript fMS Eng. 1015, Houghton Library, Cambridge, Massachusetts.

Bauderon, Brice. *Pharmacopoea*. Translated by Philemon Holland. London, 1639.

Beguin, Jean. *Elemens de Chymie*. Lyon, 1665.

Beguin, Jean. *Les Elemens de Chymie*. 3rd ed. Paris, 1624.

Beguin, Jean. *Tyrocinium Chymicum or Chymical Essays*. London, 1669.

Bertholdus, Andreas. *The Wonderfull and strange effect and vertues of a new Terra Sigillata lately found out in Germany. . . .* Translated by B. Googe. London, 1587.

Besanson, Philip. *De Ardvennae sylvae duorum admirabilium fontium effectis admirabilibus Libellus*. Paris, 1577.

Béze, Theodore de. *A shorte, learned and pithie Treatize of the Plague. . . .* Translated by J. Stockwood. London, 1580.

Biggs, Noah. *Mataeotechnia Medicinae Praxews*. London, 1651.

The boke of knowledge whether a sycke person beynge in perylle shall lyve or dye. London (1535?).

Bonham, Thomas. *The Chyrurgians Closet. . . .* London, 1630.

The Book of Quinte Essence or the Fifth Being: That is to say, Man's Heaven . . . c. 1460–70. Early English Text Society, No. 16. London, 1866.

A Booke of Soveraigne approved medicines and remedies. . . . London, 1577.

Borde, Andrew. *The Breviary of Healthe. . . .* London, 1552.

Borde, Andrew. *Here foloweth a compēdyous Regyment or a Dyetary of Helth made in Moutpyllor*. London (1542?).

B., R., esq. (Bostocke, R.). *The Difference betwene the auncient Phisicke . . . and the latter Phisicke*. London, 1585.

Boyle, Robert. *Experiments and Considerations Touching Colours*. London, 1664.

Boyle, Robert. *Short Memoirs for the Natural Experimental History of Mineral Waters Addressed by way of Letter to a Friend.* London, 1684/5.

Boyle, Robert. *The Works of the Honourable Robert Boyle.* Edited by T. Birch. 6 vols. London, 1772.

Bradwell, Stephen. *Helps for Suddain Accidents Endangering Life.* London, 1633.

Bradwell, Stephen. *Physick for the Sicknesse, Commonly called the Plague.* London, 1636.

Bradwell, Stephen. *A Watch-Man for the Pest.* London, 1625.

Brasbridge, Thomas. *The Poor Man's Jewel.* . . . London, 1579.

Brian, Thomas. *The Pisse-Prophet, Or Certain Pisse-Pot Lectures.* London, 1637.

A Briefe Discourse of the Hypostasis, or Substance of the water of Spaw. Translated from the French by G. T. London, *c.* 1600.

Bright, Timothy. *A Treatise Wherein is declared the sufficiencie of English Medicines for cure of all diseases cured with Medicine.* London, 1580.

Bruel, Walter. *Praxis Medicinae, or the Physicians Practise.* 2nd ed. London, 1639.

Brugis, Th. *The Discovery of a Proiector.* London, 1641.

Brugis, Th. *The Marrow of Physicke* . . . *a Medicamentary.* London, 1640.

Brugis, Th. *Vade Mecum: Or, a Companion for a Chyrurgian: fitted for times of peace or war.* London, 1651.

Brunschwig, Hieronymus. *A most excellent . . . homist apothecarye.* . . . Translated by Ihon Hollybush. Collen, 1561.

Brunschwig, Hieronymus. *The noble experyence of the vertuous handyworke of surgeri.* . . . London, 1525.

Brunschwig, Hieronymus. *The vertuose boke of distyllacyon.* . . . Translated by L. Andrewe. London, 1527.

Bullein, William. *Bulleins Bulwarke of defece againste all Sicknes, sornes, and woundes.* 4 parts. London, 1579.

Bullein, William. *A comfortable regiment against pleurisi.* London, 1562.

Bullein, William. *A Newe Booke entituled the Governement of Healthe.* London, 1558.

C., T. *An Hospitall for the diseased.* . . . London, 1595.

Caius, John, M.D. *The Works of John Caius, M.D., second Founder of Gonville and Caius College & Master of the College 1559-1573, with a Memoir of his Life by John Venn, Sc.D.* Edited by E. S. Roberts. Cambridge, 1912.

Cardan, Jerome. *The Book of My Life (De Vita Propria Liber).* Translated by Jean Stoner. New York, 1962.

Cardan, Jerome. *The First Book of Jerome Cardan's De Subtilitate.* Latin text, commentary, and translation by Myrtle Marguerite Cass. Williamsport, Pa., 1934.

Cardan, Jerome. *De Rerum Varietate Libri XVII*. Basel, 1557.

Cardan, Jerome. *De Subtilitate*. Nuremberg, 1550.

Cary, Walter. *A briefe Treatise called Caries farewell to Physicke*. London 1583.

Cary, Walter. *The hammer for the stone*. London, 1580.

Chaloner, Sir Thomas the younger. *A Shorte Discourse of the most rare and excellent vertue of Nitre*. . . . London, 1584.

Chauliac, Guy de. *Guydos Questions, newly corrected*. Edited by G. Baker. London, 1579.

Chauliac, Guy de. *The questyonary of Cyrurgyens*. . . . Translated by R. Coplande. London, 1542.

Chettle, Henry. *Kind-Hartes Dreame*. London, 1592.

Clapham, Henoch. *An Epistle Discoursing upon the present Pestilence*. . . . London, 1603.

Clapham, Henoch. *His Demaundes and Answeres touching the Pestilence*. . . . London(?), 1604.

Clever, William. *The Flower of Phisicke*. . . . London, 1590.

Clowes, William. *A Briefe and necessarie Treatise touching the cure of the disease called Morbus Gallicus*. . . . London, 1585.

Clowes, William. *A Profitable and Necessarie Booke of Observations for all those that are burned with the flame of Gunpowder, &c*. London, 1596.

Clowes, William. *Profitable and necessarie booke of observations*. Introductions by De Witt T. Starnes and Chauncey D. Leake. New York, 1945.

Clowes, William. *A prooved practise for all young Chirurgians, concerning burnings with Gunpowder, and woundes made with Gunshot*. London, 1588.

Clowes, William. *A Right Frutefull and Approved Treatise for the Artificiall Cure of that Malady called in Latin Struma*. London, 1602.

Clowes, William. *Selected Writings*. With an introduction and notes by F. N. L. Poynter. London, 1948.

Clowes, William. *A Short and profitable Treatise touching upon the cure of the disease called Morbus Gallicus by Unctions*. London, 1579.

Coghan, Thomas. *The haven of health*. . . . 3rd issue. London, 1589.

Cotta, John. *Cotta Contra Antonium: or an Ant-Antony*. . . . Oxford, 1623.

Cotta, John. *A Short Discoverie of the Unobserved Dangers of severall sorts of ignorant and Unconsiderable Practisers of Physicke in England*. London, 1612.

Coxe, Francis. *A Short Treatise declaringe the detestable wickedness of magicall sciences*. . . . London (1561?).

Cuffe, Henry. *The Differences of the Ages of Mans Life*. London, 1607.

Culpeper, Nicholas. *Pharmacopoeia Londinensis: or the London Dispensatory.* . . . 6th ed. London, 1659.

Culpeper, Nicholas, Gent. *A Physicall Directory; or, A translation of the London Dispensatory Made by the Colledge of Physicians in London.* London, 1649.

D., E., Dr. of Physicke. *The Copy of a Letter* . . . *The former part containeth rules for the preservation of health* . . . *The latter is a discourse of Empericks or unlearned Physitions.* London, 1606.

Dariot, Claudius. *A Briefe and most easie Introduction to the Astrologicall Judgement of the Starres.* . . . London, 1598.

Deane, Edmund. *Spadacrene Anglica, or The English Spa Fountain. The First Work on the Waters of Harrowgate.* Reprinted with an Introduction by James Rutherford, L.R.C.P. Edited and Biographical Notes by Alexander Butler, M.B. London, 1922.

Deane, Edmund (Dr. in Physicke, Oxon, dwelling in the City of York). *Spadacrene Anglica or The English Spaw-Fountains. Being a Briefe Treatise of the acide, or tart Fountaine in the Forest of Knaresborow, in the West-Riding of Yorkshire.* London, 1626.

Dee, Arthur. *Fasciculus Chemicus: or Chymicall Collections.* Translated by James Hasolle (Elias Ashmole). London, 1650.

Dee, John. *The private Diary of Dr. J. D.* [from 1554 to 1601] . . . Edited by J. O. Halliwell. Camden Society, No. 19. London, 1842.

Dieterich, Helvig. *Elogium Coelestium et Terrestrium, Macrocosmi & Microcosmi.* Argentorati, 1627.

Dieterich, Helvig. *Novus Orbis.* Argentorati, 1631.

A discourse of the medicine called Mithridatium. London, 1585.

Distillers of London [Company of]. *The Distiller of London.* London, 1639.

Donne, John. *Complete Poetry and Selected Prose.* Bloomsbury, 1929.

Duchesne, Joseph (Josephus Quercetanus). *A Breefe Aunswere of Josephus Quercetanus* . . . *to the exposition of Iacobus Aubertus Vindonis, concerning the original and causes of Mettalles. Set foorth against chimistes.* . . . *Another exquisite and plaine Treatise of the same Josephus, concerning the Spagericall preparations and use of minerall, animall, and vegitable Medicines.* Translated and expanded by John Hester. London, 1591.

Duchesne, Joseph. *Le Grand Miroir du Monde.* Paris, 1595.

Duchesne, Joseph (Josephus Quercetanus). *The Practise of Chymicall, and Hermeticall Physicke for the preservation of health.* Translated by Th. Tymme, Minister. London, 1605.

Duchesne, Joseph (Quercetanus). *Liber de Priscorum Philosophorum verae medicinae materia.* S. Gervasii, 1603.

Duchesne, Joseph. *The Sclopotarie* . . . *or His booke containing the cure of wounds*. Translated by John Hester. London, 1590.

Duchesne, Joseph (Quercetanus). *Ad Veritatem Hermeticae Medicinae ex Hippocratis veterúmque decretis ac Therapeusi*. Paris, 1604.

Du Laurens, Andre. *A Discourse of the preservation of the Sight*. London, 1599.

Edwards, E. *The Cure of All Sorts of Fevers*. . . . London, 1638.

Elyot, Sir Thomas. *The castel of helthe (1541), Together with the title page and preface of the edition of 1539*. New York, 1937.

Erastus, Thomas. *Disputationes De Medicina nova Paracelsi. Pars 1 in qua quae de remediis superstitiosis et magicis curationibus prodidit praecipue examinantur*. Basel, s.a. [1572].

Erastus, Thomas. *Disputationes de Medicina Nova Paracelsi. Pars altera in qua Philosophiae Paracelsicae Principia et Elementa explorantur*. s.l., 1572.

Especiall Observations and Approved Physicall Rules; which have (heretofore) beene well Tryed and Experienced, in the last heavy and grievous time of the Pestilence. London, 1625.

Evans, John. *The Universall Medicine: or the Vertues of the Antimoniall Cup*. . . . London, 1634.

Falloppius, Gabrielis (Mutinensis). *De Medicatis Aquis atque de Fossilibus*. Venice, 1569.

Fioravanti, Leonardo. *A Compendium of the Rationall Secretes* . . . *of the hidden vertues of sondrie vegitables, animalles, and mineralls*. Translated by John Hester. London, 1582.

Fioravanti, Leonardo. *A Ioyfull Iewell*. . . . Translated by John Hester. London, 1579.

Fioravanti, Leonardo. *A short discourse* . . . *uppon Chirurgerie*. Translated by J. Hester. London, 1580.

Fioravanti, Leonardo. *Three Exact Pieces of Leonard Phioravant Knight and Doctor in Physick, viz.: His Rationall Secrets & Chirurgery, Reviewed and Revived, Together with a Book of Excellent Experiments and Secrets, Collected out of the Practises of severall Expert Men in both Faculties, Whereunto is Annexed Paracelsus his One hundred and fourteen Experiments With certain Excellent works of B. G. a Portu Aquitans*. . . . Translated by John Hester. London, 1652.

Flammel, Nicholas. *His Exposition of the Hieroglyphicall Figures which he caused to bee painted upon an Arch in St. Innocents Church-yard, in Paris. Together with The secret Booke of Artephius, and the Epistle of John Pontanus*. Translated by Eirenaeus Orandus. London, 1624.

Fludd, Robert. *Anatomiae Amphitheatrum effigie triplici, more et conditione varia designatum*. Frankfort, 1623.

Fludd, Robert. *Apologia Compendiaria Fraternitatem de Rosea Cruce Suspicionis et Infamiae Maculis Aspersam, Veritatis quasi Fluctibus abluens et abstergens.* Leiden, 1616.

Fludd, Robert. *Clavis Philosophiae et Alchymiae Fluddanae. sive Roberti Fluddi Armigeri, et Medicinae Doctoris, ad Epistolicam Petri Gassendi Theologi Exercitationem Responsum.* Frankfort, 1633.

Fludd, Robert. *Doctor Fludds Answer unto M. Foster. Or, the Squeesing of Parson Fosters Sponge, ordained by him for the wiping away of the Weapon-Salve.* London, 1631.

Fludd, Robert. *Integrum Morborum Mysterium: Sive Medicinae Catholicae Tomi Primi Tractatus Secundus.* Frankfort, 1631.

Fludd, Robert. *Medicina Catholica, seu Mysticum Artis Medicandi Sacrarium in Tomos diuisum duos.* Vol. 1. Frankfort, 1629.

Fludd, Robert, Esq. *Mosaicall Philosophy: Grounded upon the Essentiall Truth or Eternal Sapience.* London, 1659.

Fludd, Robert. *Philosophia sacra & vere Christiana seu Meteorologia Cosmica.* Frankfort, 1626.

Fludd, Robert. *Pulsus, seu nova et arcana pulsuum historia, e Sacro Fonte Radicaliter Extracta, nec non Medicorum Ethnicorum Dictis & authoritate comprobata.* Frankfort (1631?).

Fludd, Robert. *Sophiae Cum Moria Certamen, In quo Lapis Lydius A Falso Structore, Fr. Marino Mersenno, Monacho, Reprobatus, celeberrima Voluminis sui Babylonici (in Genesin) figmenta accurate examinat.* Frankfort, 1629.

Fludd, Robert. *Summum Bonum.* Frankfort, 1629.

Fludd, Robert. *Tomi Secundi Tractatus Secundus De Praeternaturali Utriusque Mundi Historia In Sectiones tres divisa.* Frankfort, 1621.

Fludd, Robert. *Tomus Secundus de Supernaturali, Naturali, Praeternaturali et contranaturali Microcosmi historia, in Tractatus tres distributa.* Oppenheim, 1619.

Fludd, Robert. *Tractatus Apologeticus Integritatem Societatis De Rosea Cruce defendens.* Lugduni Batavorum, 1617.

Fludd, Robert. *Tractatus Secundus De Naturae Simia seu Technica macrocosmi historia.* 2nd ed. Frankfort, 1624.

Fludd, Robert. *Utriusque Cosmi Maioris scilicet et Minoris Metaphysica, Physica atque Technica.* Oppenheim, 1617.

Folius, Cecilio. *Sanguinis a dextro in sinistrum cordis Ventriculum.* Venice, 1639.

Forrest, Peter. *The Arraignment of Urines. . . .* Translated by James Hart. London, 1623.

Foster, William. *Hoplocrisma-Spongus: or a Sponge to wipe away the Weapon-Salve.* London, 1631.

French, John. *The York-shire Spaw, or a Treatise of four Famous Medicinal Wells.* London, 1652.

Fuchs, Leonard. *A most worthie practise of . . . L. Fuchsius. . . .* London, 1562.

Gaebelkhover, Oswald. *The Boock of Physicke. . . .* Translated by C. Battus. Dorte, 1599.

Galen. *Certaine Workes of Galens called Methodus Medendi. . . .* Translated by T. Gale. London, 1586.

Gassendi, Pierre. "De Septo cordis pervio observatio", in Séverin Pineau, *De integritatis et corruptionis Virginum notis.* Lugduni Batavorum, 1641.

Gassendi, Pierre. *Epistolica exercitatio in qua principia philosophiae Roberti Fluddi, medici, reteguntur, et ad recentes illius libras adversus R.P.F. Marinum Mersennum . . . respondetur.* Paris, 1630.

Gassendi, Pierre. *Opera Omnia.* 6 vols. Florence, 1727.

Geber. *The Works of Geber.* Translated by Richard Russell, edited and with an introduction by E. J. Holmyard. London, 1928.

Geminus, Thomas. *Compendiosa totius Anatomie delineatio. . . .* London, 1545.

Gerarde, John. *The Herball or Generall Historie of Plantes.* London, 1597.

Gesner, Conrad. *Bibliotheca Universalis.* Tiguri, 1545.

Gesner, Conrad. *Euonymus . . . Liber secundus.* Tigurini, 1569.

Gesner, Conrad. *The Newe Jewell of Health.* Translated by Thomas Hill and George Baker. London, 1576.

Gesner, Conrad. *The practise of the new and old phisicke.* Translated by Thomas Hill and George Baker. London, 1599.

Gesner, Conrad. *The Treasure of Euonymus; conteyninge the wonderfull hid secretes of nature.* Translated by P. Morwyng. London, 1559.

Goeurot, J. *The Regiment of Life.* Translated by Thomas Phaer. London, 1544.

Gordon, D. *Pharmaco-Pinax.* Aberdeen, 1625.

Gratarolus, Gulielmus. *A Direction for the Health of Magistrates and Students.* Translated by T. Newton. London, 1574.

Guibert, Philibert. *The Charitable Physitian.* Translated by T. W. London, 1639.

Gwinne, Matthew. *In Assertorem Chymicae, sed Verae Medicinae Desertorem, Fra. Anthoniam.* London, 1611.

Gyer, Nicholas. *The English Phlebotomy.* London, 1592.

Hall, John. *A most excellent and learned woorke of chirurgerie . . . also agains the beastly abusers, both of chyrurgerie and phisicke in our tyme.* London, 1565

Harington, Sir John. *The Englishmans Doctor. Or the Schoole of Salerne. . . .* London, 1608.

Hart, James (of Northampton). *The Anatomie of Urines.* . . . London, 1625.

Hart, James (of Northampton). *KΛINIKH, Or the Diet of the Diseased.* London, 1633.

Harvey, Gabriel. *Pierce's Supererogation, or a new Prayse of the old Asse.* London, 1593.

Harvey, William. *The Circulation of the Blood and Other Writings.* Everyman edition. London, 1952.

Harvey, William. *Movement of the Heart and Blood in Animals.* Translated by Kenneth J. Franklin. Oxford, 1957.

Harvey, William. *Works.* London, 1847.

Hastler, Thomas. *An Antidote Against the Plague.* London, 1625.

Heer, Henry de. *Les Fontaines de Spa.* Liège, 1616.

Heer, Henry de. *Les Fontaines de Spa.* (Dernière édition.) Liège, 1630.

Heer, Henry de. *Les Fontaines de Spa.* (Dernière édition.) Liège, 1646.

Heer, Henry de. *Les Fontaines de Spa Descrites.* (Dernière édition.) Liège, 1654.

Helmont, Johann Baptista van. *Opera Omnia.* Frankfort, 1682.

Helmont, Johann Baptista van. *Oriatrike or, Physick Refined.* Translated by John Chandler. London, 1662.

Henry, William. *The Elements of Experimental Chemistry.* First American from the 8th London edition. 2 vols. Philadelphia, 1819.

Here begynneth a newe boke of medecynes intytulyd the treasure of pore men. London (1526?).

Hermanus, Phillippus. *An excellent Treatise teaching howe to cure the French Pockes . . . Drawen out of the Bookes of that learned Doctor and Prince of Phisitions, Theophrastus Paracelsus.* Translated by John Hester. London, 1590.

Herring, Francis, Dr. in Physicke. *A Modest Defence of the Caveat given to the Wearers of impoisoned Amulets, as Preservatives from the Plague.* London, 1604.

Hippocrates. *Prognostication drawen out of Ipocras.* . . . London (1530?).

H., S. [Stephen Hobbs]. *Margarita Chyrurgica: Containing a Compendious Practise of Chyrurgerie.* London, 1610.

Hutton, Ulrich von. *De morbo gallico.* Translated by T. Paynell. London, 1533.

Hutton, Ulrich von. *Of the wood called Guaiacum that healeth the French pockes.* . . . Translated by T. Paynell. London, 1536.

John XXI, Pope. *The treasurie of healthe.* . . . London (1550?).

Johnson, Thomas. *Mercurius Botanicus; huis accessit de Thermis Bathonicis.* London, 1634.

Johnson, Thomas. *Thermae Bathonicae, sive Earum descriptio, Vires, utendi tempus, modus, &c.* London, 1634.

Jones, John. *The Arte and Science of preseruing Bodie and Soule in Healthe, Wisdome, and Catholike Religion.* London, 1579.

Jones, John. *The Bathes of Bathes Ayde.* London, 1572.

Jones, John. *The Benefit of the auncient bathes of Buckstones.* London, 1572.

Jones, John. *A briefe . . . discourse of the naturall beginning of all growing and living things; heate, generation . . . use and abuse of phisicke, preservation, etc. . . . Here unto is annexed a . . . work, entituled, Galens booke of Elements . . . in theende whereof is adjoyned two other bookes [The of Bathes Ayde, The Benefit of the auncient bathes of Buckstones] Bathes containing the nature . . . of all the Bathes in England, etc.* 4 parts. London, 1572–74.

Jones, John. *The Dyall of Agues.* London, 1566.

Jones, John. *Galens Bookes of Elementes . . . Confuting as well the errours of all them that went before time, as that hath, or shal folowe here after of Paracelsians.* London, 1574.

Jonson, Ben. *The Alchemist.* Edited by Charles M. Hathaway, Jr. Yale Studies in English. New York, 1903.

Jordan, Thomas. *De Aquis Medicatis Moravia.* Frankfort, 1586.

Jorden, Edward. *A briefe discourse of a disease called the Suffocation of the Mother, written upon occasion which hath beene of late taken thereby, to suspect possession of an evill spirit or some such like supernaturall power. Wherein is declared that divers strange actions and passions of the body of man, which . . . are imputed to the Divell, have their true natural causes, and do accompanie this disease.* London, 1603.

Jorden, Edward (Dr. in Physicke). *A Discourse of Naturall Bathes and Minerall Waters.* London, 1631.

Jorden, Edward. *A Discourse of Natural Bathes and Mineral Waters. . . . The second edition in many points enlarged.* London, 1632.

Jorden, Edward. *A Discourse of Natural Bathes and Mineral Waters. . . . A Quere concerning Bath-Water at Bathe . . . an Appendix concerning Bathe . . . by Thomas Guidott, M.B.* 4th ed. London, 1673.

Kellwaye, Simon. *A Defensative against the Plague.* London, 1593.

Kepler, Ioannes. *Harmonices Mundi Libri V.* Contains an "Appendix habet comparationem huius Operis cum Harmonices C. Ptolemaei libro III, cumque Roberti de Fluctibus, dicti Flud. Medici Oxoniensis speculationibus Harmonices, operi de Macrocosmo & Microcosmo insertis". Lincii Austriae, 1619.

The Key to unknowne Knowledge. . . . London, 1599.

Lambye, John Baptista. *A Revelation of the Secret Spirit. Declaring the Most*

Concealed secret of Alchymie. Translated by R. N. E., gentleman. London, 1623.

Langham, Wm. *The Garden of Health.* London, 1597.

Langton, Christopher. *An introduction into phisicke.* London (1550?).

Langton, Christopher. *A very brefe treatise, ordrely declaring the pricipal parts of phisick.* . . . London, 1547.

Lemery, Nicholas. *A Course of Chymistry.* Translated by Walter Harris, M.D. 2nd ed., from the 5th French ed. London, 1686.

Libavius, Andreas. "De Iudicio Aquarum Mineralium, et horum quae cum illis inveniuntur," *Alchemia.* Frankfort, 1597.

Lodge, Thomas. *A Treatise of the Plague.* London, 1603.

Lowe, Peter. *The Whole Course of Chirurgerie.* London, 1597.

M., J. *The General Practise of Medicine.* Edinburgh, 1634.

Maier, Michael. *Themis Aurea. The Laws of the Fraternity of the Rosie Crosse.* London, 1656.

Mayerne, Sir Theodore Turquet de. *Opera medica, complectentia consilia, epistolas, et observationes, pharmacopeam, variasque medica mentuum formulas.* London, 1703.

Mediolano, Joannes de. *Regimen Sanitatis Salerni.* Translated by T. Paynell. London, 1528.

Mersenne, P. Marin. *Correspondance du P. Marin Mersenne.* Edited by Cornelius De Waard and René Pintard. 4 vols. Paris, 1932–55.

Mersenne, P. Marin. *La Vérité des Sciences Contre Les Septiques ou Pyrrhoniens.* Paris, 1625.

Mexia, Pedro. *A Delectable Dialogue. Wherein is contayned a Pleasaunt Disputation between two Spanish Gentlemen, concerning Phisick and Phisitions.* . . . Translated by T. Newton. London, 1580.

Miropsius, Nicolas (called Prepositas). *Prepositas his practise, wherein are approved medicines.* London, 1588.

Moffett, Thomas. "De Jure et Praestantia Chemicorum Medicamentorum", *Theatrum Chemicum.* Edited by L. Zetzner. Argentorati, 1659.

Moffett, Thomas. *Health's Improvement.* London, 1655.

Moffett, Thomas. *Insectorum sive Minimorum Animalium Theatrum* . . . *ad vivum expressis Iconibus super quingentis illustratum.* London, 1634.

Monardes, Nicholas. *Joyfull newes out of the newe founde worlde.* 3rd printing. London, 1596.

Montagnana, Bartolomeo. *Consilia CCCV.* Venice, 1564.

Montagnana, Bartolomeo. "Tractatus tres de balneis patavinis", *Consilia.* Venice, 1497.

Montpellier. *The practyse of Cyrurgyons of Mountpyller; and of others that never came there.* London (1540?).

Moore, Philip. *The Hope of Health*. London, 1565.

Morus, Horatius. *Tables of Surgerie*. . . . Translated by R. Caldwall, edited by E. Caldwall. London, 1585.

Moulton, Thomas. *This is the Myrrour or Glass of Helth*. . . . London (1539?).

M[ure]., A. *Πιδαξ Πετρεια, or The discoverie of S. Peters Well, at Peterhead in Scotland*. Edinburgh, 1636.

A myrrour or glasse for them that be syke. Southwarke (1536?).

Nashe, Thomas. *The Terrors of the Night*. London, 1594.

l'Obel, Matthias de. *In G. Rondellettii . . . Pharmaceuticam Officinam Animadversiones*. London, 1605.

l'Obel, Matthias de. *Stirpium Adversaria Nova*. London, 1571.

Oberndorff, John. *The Anatomyes of the True Physition, and Counterfeit Mountebank*. . . . Translated by Francis Herring. London, 1602.

Paracelsus, Theophrastus. *The first (and second) part of the Key of Philosophie*. Translated by John Hester. London, 1596.

Paracelsus. *The Secrets of Physick and Philosophy . . . First written in the German Tongue by . . . Theophrastus Paracelsus and now published in the English Tongue by John Hester, Practitioner in the Art of Distillation*. London, 1633.

Paynell, Thomas (tr.). *A much profitable Treatise against the Pestilence*. London, 1534.

Peiresc, Nicolas-Claude Fabri de. *Lettres De Peiresc Publiées par Philippe Tamizey de Larroque . . . Tome Quatrième: Lettres de Peiresc à Borrilly, à Bouchard et à Gassendi. Lettres de Gassendi à Peiresc, 1626–1637*. Paris, 1893.

Petty, Sir William. "An Apparatus to the History of the Common Practices of Dying", in Thomas Sprat, *The History of the Royal Society of London*. 3rd ed. London, 1722.

Philiatros, or, The Copie of an Epistle, wherein sundry fitting Considerations are propounded to a young Student of Physicke. London, 1615.

Platte, Hugh. *The Jewell House of Art and Nature*. 3 parts. London, 1594.

Plattes, Gabriel. *A Discovery of Infinite Treasure*. London, 1639.

Plattes, Gabriel. *A Discovery of Subterraneall Treasure, viz. of all manner of Mines and Minerals, from Gold to Coale*. London, 1639.

Pliny. *The Elder Pliny's Chapters on Chemical Subjects*. Edited and translated by Kenneth C. Bailey. 2 vols. London, 1929–32.

Pliny. *Historiae Naturalis Libri XXXVII*. 5 vols. Biponti, 1783–84.

Plutarch. *The governance of good helthe*. London, 1530.

Plutarch. *The precepts of Plutarch for the preservation of good healthe*. Translated by J. Hales. London, 1543.

Porta, John Baptista. *Natural Magick*. New York, 1957.

Primerose, James, Dr. of Physicke. *The Antimoniall Cup twice cast: Or, A Treatise concerning the Antimoniall Cup.* Translated by Robert Wittie. London, 1640.

Primerose, James. *Exercitationes et Animadversiones in Librum De Motu Cordis et Circulatione Sanguis.* London, 1630.

Primerose, James. *Popular Errours, Or the Errours of the People in Physick.* Translated by Robert Wittie. London, 1651.

Rawlin, Thomas. *Admonitio Pseudo-Chymicis seu Alphabetarium Philosophicum.* London, c. 1610.

Rawlin, Thomas. *A Warning to the False Chymists Or the Philosophicall Alphabet.* British Museum Sloane Ms 3643, ff 14–92.

Raynalde, Thomas. *A compendious declaration of the . . . vertues of a certain lateli inventid oile. . . .* Venice, 1551.

Read, Alexander. *The Chirurgicall Lectures of Tumors and Ulcers.* London, 1635.

Read, Alexander. *A Treatise of the First Part of Chirurgerie . . . Containing the methodical doctrine of Wounds.* London, 1638.

Record, Robert. *The Urinal of Physick.* London, 1548.

Rhumel, Johann [Salomon Raphael]. *Avicula Hermetis Catholica, De Mercurio Sulphure et Sale Philosophorum in uno subjecto. . . .* London, 1638.

Rhumel, Johann. *Canticum Canticorum. Quod est Schelemonis De Medicina Universali.* London, 1638.

Rhumel, Johann. *Compendium Hermeticum De Macrocosmo et Microcosmo. . . .* London (1638?).

Ripley, George. *The Compound of Alchymy. . . .* London, 1591.

Rosetti, G. V. *Plictho de Larte de Tentori che Insegna Tenger Pani Telle Banbasi et Sede Si Per Larthe Magiore Come per la Comane.* Venice, 1540.

Rotuli Parliamentorum ut et Petitiones, et Placita in Parliamento. 7 vols. London, 1832.

Rowzee, Lodowick. *The Queens Wells.* London, 1630.

Royal College of Physicians. *Certain necessary Directions, as well for preventing the Infection. . . .* London, 1636.

Royal College of Physicians. *The Kings Medicines for the Plague Prescribed for the yeare 1604. . . .* London, 1630.

Royal College of Physicians. *Pharmacopoeia Londinensis of 1618 Reproduced in Facsimile with a Historical Introduction by George Urdang.* Madison, 1944.

Royal College of Physicians. *Pharmacopoeia Londinensis in quo Medicamenta Antiqua et Nova usitatissima. . . .* 2nd ed. London, 1618.

Royal College of Physicians. *Pharmacopoeia Londinensis in quo Medicamenta Antiqua ut Nova usitatissima.* 3rd ed. London, 1627.

Royal College of Physicians. *Pharmacopoeia Londinensis.* . . . 5th ed. London, 1639.

Royal College of Physicians. *Pharmocopoeia Londinensis.* . . . London, 1650.

Russel, Thomas. *Diacatholicon Aureum: or A generall powder of Gold, purging all offensive humours in mans bodie.* London, 1602.

Sadler, John. *Enchiridion Medicum: An Enchiridion of the Art of Physick.* . . . Translated and revised by Robert Turner. London, 1657.

Sadler, John. *Praxis Medicorum.* Preface by Alexander Read. London, 1637.

Sala, Angelus. *Opiologia; or, A Treatise concerning the Nature, properties, true preparation and safe use and administration of Opium.* Translated and enlarged by Tho. Bretnor. London, 1618.

Savonarola, Johannes Michael. *De balneis et termis naturalibus omnibus ytalie.* Ferrara, 10 November 1485.

Savonarola, Johannes Michael. *Practica Canonica De Febribus . . . eiusdem de Pulsibus, Urinis, Egestimibus, Vermibus, Balneis Omnibus Italiae.* Venice, 1552.

Securis, John. *A Detection & Querimonie of the daily enormities & abuses committed in physick.* London, 1566.

Sennert, Daniel. *The Weapon-Salves Maladie:* . . . London, 1637.

Severinus, Petrus. *Idea Medicinae Philosophicae.* 3rd ed. Hagae Comitis, 1660.

Short, Thomas (M.D. of Sheffield). *The Natural, Experimental, and Medicinal History of the Mineral Waters of Derbyshire, Lincolnshire, and Yorkshire, Particularly those of Scarborough . . . To which are added Large Marginal Notes, containing a Methodical Abstract of all the Treatises hitherto published on these Waters . . . and also Four Copper Plates representing the Crystals of the Salts of Thirty four of those Waters.* London, 1734.

Simpson, W. *A Discourse of the Sulphur-Bath at Knaresbrough in York-Shire.* London, 1675.

Simpson, W. (Philo-Chymico-Medicus). *Hydrologia chymica: or, the Chymical Anatomy of the Scarbrough and other Spaws in York-Shire.* London, 1669.

Simpson, W. (Dr. in Physick and Practitioner at Wakefield in Yorkshire). *Hydrological Essayes: or a Vindication of Hydrologia Chymica [against Wittie's reply] . . . Together with a return to some Queries propounded by the ingenious Dr. Dan. Foot, concerning Mineral Waters. To which is annexed An Answer to Dr. Tunstal's Book, concerning the Scarbrough Spaw.* London, 1670.

Simpson, W. *Philosophical Dialogues Concerning the Principles of Natural Bodies Wherein The Principle of the Old and New Philosophy are stated, and the New demonstrated, more agreeable to Reason, from Mechanical Experiments and its usefulness to the benefit of Man-kind.* London, 1677.

Solenander, Reine. *De Caloris Fontium medicatorum causa, eorum temperatione.* Lugduni, 1558.

Sprat, Thomas. *The History of the Royal Society of London.* 3rd ed. London, 1722.

Stanhope, Michael. *Cures Without Care, or a Summons to all Such Who Find Little or no helpe by the use of ordinary physick to repaire to the Northerne Spaw.* London, 1632.

Stanhope, Michael. *Newes out of York-Shire: or, an Account of a Journey, in the True Discovery of a soveraigne Minerall, Medicinall Water.* London, 1626.

Starkey, George. *Natures Explication and Helmont's Vindication.* London, 1651.

The Statutes at Large from the First year of Queen Mary to the Thirty-fifth year of Queen Elizabeth inclusive. Edited by Danby Pickering. Cambridge, 1763.

The Statutes at Large from the Thirty-second year of King Henry VIII to the Seventh year of King Edward VI inclusive. Edited by Danby Pickering. Cambridge, 1763.

Stubbes, Philip. *The Anatomie of Abuses.* London, 1583.

T., A. *A Rich Storehouse or Treasury for the Diseased.* 4th ed. (1st ed. 1596). London, 1607.

Terrasson, P. (Dr. in Med.). *Description et Relation Fidele de la nature, proprietez et usage de la Fontaine Mineral Nouvellement De Couverte au Terroir de la Ville de Dye.* Grenoble, 1672.

Thornborough, John, Bp. of Bristol. *Letter of Chemistry to the right Ho^{ble} the Lady Knowles . . . dated 1614.* Sloane Ms 1799 British Museum.

Thornborough, John, Bp. of Bristol. Λιθοθεωρικος, *sive Nihil, Aliquid, Omnia, Antiquorum Sapientum Vivis coloribus depicta, Philosophico-theologicèe.* Oxford, 1621.

Thurneisser zum Thurn, Leonhart. *Pison.* Frankfurt on der Oder, 1572.

Tonstall, George. *A New-Years-Gift for Doctor Witty; or the Dissector Anatomized: Which is a reply to the Discourse Intituled An Answer to all that Doctor Tonstall has writ or shall hereafter Write, against Scarbrough Spaw.* London, 1672.

Tonstall, George (Doctor of Physick). *Scarbrough Spaw Spagyrically Anatomized.* London, 1670.

Tooker, Wm. *Charisma seu Donum Sanationis. . . .* London, 1597.

Turner, Peter. *The Opinion of Peter Turner Doct. in Physicke, concerning Amulets, or Plague Cakes. . . .* London, 1603.

Turner, William (Dean of Wells). *A Booke of the natures and properties as well of the bathes in England as of other bathes in Germanye and Italye.* Collen, 1568.

Turner, William. *The seconde parte of Guilliam Turners herball* . . . *A Booke of the natures and properties as well of the bathes in England as of other bathes in Germanye and Italye.* Collen, 1562.

Tymme, Thomas. *A Dialogue Philosophicall, Wherein Natures Secret Closet is Opened, and the Cause of All Motion in Nature Shewed out of Matter and Forme, tending to mount mans minde from Nature to Supernaturall and Celestiall promotion: And how all things exist in the number of three. Together with the wittie invention of an Artificiall perpetuall motion, presented to the Kings most excellent Maiestie. All which are discoursed betweene two speakers, Philadelph, and Theophrast, brought together by Thomas Tymme, Professour of Divinitie.* London, 1612.

Valentinus, Petrus. *Enchiridion Medicum: Containing an Epitome of the Whole Course of Physicke.* London, 1608.

Vaughn, Sir William. *Naturall and artificiall Directions for Health, derived from the best philosophers, as well moderne, as auncient.* London, 1600.

Vaughn, Sir William. *The Newlanders Cure.* London, 1630.

Venner, Tobias. *Via Recta ad Vitam Longam* . . . *Whereunto is annexed a necessary and compendious Treatise of the famous Baths of Bathe.* 3rd ed. London, 1628.

Verro, Sebastian. *Physicorum Libri X.* London, 1581.

Vicary, Thomas. *The English-Mans Treasure.* . . . 8th ed. London, 1633.

Vigo, Joannes de. *The lytell practyce of J. de Vigo in Medycyne* . . . *for the helth of the body of man.* London (1540?).

Vigo, Joannes de. *The most excellent workes of chirurgerye made and set forth by maister J. Vignon.* . . . Translated by B. Traheron. London, 1543.

Vitruvius. *The Ten Books on Architecture.* Cambridge, Mass., 1914.

W., G. (?). *Newes out of Cheshire of the new found well.* London, 1600.

W., I. *The copie of a letter sent by a learned Physician to his friend, wherein are detected the manifold errors used hitherto of the Apothecaries.* . . . London, 1586.

W., O. *An Epitome of Most Experienced, Excellent, and Profitable Secrets appertaining to Physicke and Chirurgery.* . . . Preface by Alexander Read. London, 1652.

Walkington, Thomas. *The Optick Glasse of Humors.* . . . London, 1607.

Widman, Johannes (dicti Mechinger). *Tractatus de balneis thermarum ferinarum (vulgo Uuildbaden) perutilis balneari volentibus ibidem.* Tubingae, 1513.

Willis, Thomas. *Practise of Physick.* Translated by S. Pordage. London, 1684.

Willis, Timothy. *Praepositiones Tentationum: Sive Propaedeumata De Vitis et Faecunditate Compositorum naturalium: Quae sunt elementa chymica.* London, 1615.

Willis, Timothy, Apprentice in Phisicke. *The Search for Causes. Contayning a Theophysicall Investigation of the Possibilitie of Transmutatorie Alchemie.* London, 1616.

Wingfield, Henry. *A compendious . . . treatise . . . conteynynge certeyne preceptes necessary to the preservacion of healthe, and long continuance of the same.* London, 1598.

Wirtzung, Christopher. *Praxis medicinae universalis, or a general practise of physicke.* . . . Translated by J. Mosan. London, 1598.

Wittie, Robert. *Pyrologia Mimica, or, an Answer to Hydrologia Chymica of William Simpson.* London, 1669.

Wittie, Robert. *Scarbrough Spagyrical Anatomizer dissected.* London, 1672.

Wittie, Robert (Dr. in Physick). *Scarbrough Spaw, or a Description of the Nature and Vertues of the Spaw at Scarbrough in Yorkshire.* London, 1660.

Wittie, Robert. *Scarbrough-Spaw: or a Description of the Nature and Vertues of the Spaw at Scarbrough Yorkshire . . . Corrected and augmented throughout the whole.* York, 1667.

Wood, John. *Practicae Medicinae liber, vocatus Amalgama.* London, 1596.

Wood, Owen. *An Alphabetical Book of Physical Secrets.* . . . Preface by Alexander Read. London, 1639.

Woodall, John, Mr. in Chirurgery. *The Surgions mate or a Treatise Discovering faithfully and plainely the contents of the Surgions Chest, the uses of the Instruments, the vertues and operations of the Medicines. . . . With a Briefe Explanation of Sal, Sulphur and Mercury: with certaine characters, and tearmes of Arte.* London, 1617.

Woodall, John. *The Surgeons Mate: or military & domestique surgery.* London, 1639. 3rd ed. London, 1655.

Zetzner, L. (ed.). *Theatrum Chemicum.* 6 vols. Argentorati, 1659–61.

2. SECONDARY SOURCES

Allen, Phyllis. "Medical education in 17th century England", *Journal of the History of Medicine and Allied Sciences, 1* (1946), 115–43.

Arber, Agnes (Mrs.). *Herbals: their origin and evolution.* Cambridge, 1938.

Armitage, Angus. *The World of Copernicus.* New York, 1951.

Aschner, B. "Paracelsus as a Pioneer of Medical Science", *The Aryan Path, 1* (1930), 249–53.

Baas, Joh. Hermann. *Outline of the History of Medicine and The Medical Profession.* Translated by H. E. Handerson. New York, 1889.

Barrett, C. R. B. *The History of the Society of Apothecaries of London.* London, 1905.

Bayon, H. P. "Paracelsus: personality, doctrines and his alleged influence in the reform of medicine", *Proceedings of the Royal Society of Medicine*, 35 (1941), 69–76.

✓ Bayon, H. P. "William Gilbert (1544–1603), Robert Fludd (1574–1637), and William Harvey (1578–1657), as Medical Exponents of Baconian Doctrines", *Proceedings of the Royal Society of Medicine*, 32 (1938), 31–42.

Bayon, H. P. "William Harvey, Physician and Biologist: His Precursors, Opponents, and Successors", *Annals of Science*, 3 (1938), 59–119, 435–59, and 4 (1939), 65–107.

Berthelot, Marcelin. *Collection des anciens alchimistes grecs.* 3 vols. Paris, 1887–88.

Berthelot, Marcelin. *Introduction à l'étude de la chimie des anciens et du moyen âge.* Paris, 1889.

Berthelot, Marcelin. *La chimie au moyen âge.* 3 vols. Paris, 1893.

Berthelot, Marcelin. *Les origines de l'alchemie.* Paris, 1885.

Boas[Hall], Marie. "Acid and alkali in seventeenth-century chemistry", *Archives Internationales d'Histoire des Sciences*, 35 (1956), 13–28.

Boas[Hall], Marie. *Robert Boyle and Seventeenth-Century Chemistry.* Cambridge, 1958.

Bolton, H. C. *Evolution of the Thermometer, 1592–1743.* Easton, Pa., 1900.

Bougerel, Joseph. *Vie de Pierre Gassendi, prévôt de l'église de Digne.* Paris, 1737.

Brunn, Walter A. L. von. "Zur Elementenlehre des Paracelsus", *Sudhoffs Archiv für Geschichte der Medizin*, 34 (1941), 35–51.

Butterfield, Herbert. *The Origins of Modern Science 1300–1800.* New York, 1952.

Camden, Carroll, Jr. "Astrology in Shakespeare's Day", *Isis*, 19 (1933), 26–73.

Camden, Carroll, Jr. "Elizabethan Astrological Medicine", *Annals of Medical History*, New Series, 2 (1930), 217–26.

Carlton, W. J. *Timothy Bright.* London, 1911.

Chevalier, D. A. G. "The 'Antimony-War'—A Dispute Between Montpellier and Paris", *Ciba Symposia*, 2 (1940), 418–23.

Clagett, Marshall. *Greek Science in Antiquity.* New York, 1955.

Coffin, C. M. *John Donne and the New Philosophy.* New York, 1937.

Copeman, W. S. C. *Doctors and Disease in Tudor Times.* London, 1960.

Cornford, Francis M. *Plato's Cosmology. The Timaeus of Plato translated with a running commentary.* New York, 1957.

Craven, J. B. *Doctor Robert Fludd.* Kirkwall, 1902.

Creighton, C. *History of Epidemics in Britain.* London, 1891–94.

Dalton, John C. "Galen and Paracelsus", *New York Medical Journal*, May, 1873.

Darmstaedter, Ernst. "Paracelsus und die Einführung chemischer Präparate als Heilmittel", in *Georg Sticker Festgabe*. Berlin, 1930.

Debus, Allen G. "The Aerial Niter in the Sixteenth and Early Seventeenth Centuries", *Actes du Dixième Congrès International d'Histoire des Sciences* (2 vols., Paris, 1964), *2*, 835–39.

Debus, Allen G. "An Elizabethan History of Medical Chemistry", *Annals of Science*, *18* (1962), 1–29.

Debus, Allen G. "Gabriel Plattes and his Chemical Theory of the Formation of the Earth's Crust", *Ambix*, *9* (1961), 162–65.

Debus, Allen G. "John Woodall, Paracelsian Surgeon", *Ambix*, *10* (1962), 108–18.

Debus, Allen G. "The Paracelsian Aerial Niter", *Isis*, *55* (1964), 43–61.

Debus, Allen G. "The Paracelsian Compromise in Elizabethan England", *Ambix*, *8* (1960), 71–97.

Debus, Allen G. "Paracelsian Doctrine in English Medicine", in *Chemistry in the Service of Medicine*, ed. F. N. L. Poynter. London, 1963.

Debus, Allen G. "Pierre Gassendi and his 'Scientific Expedition' of 1640", *Archives Internationales d'Histoire des Sciences*, *6* (1963), 129–42.

Debus, Allen G. "Robert Fludd and the Circulation of the Blood", *Journal of the History of Medicine and Allied Sciences*, *16* (1961), 374-93.

Debus, Allen G. "Robert Fludd and the Use of Gilbert's *De Magnete* in the Weapon-Salve Controversy", *Journal of the History of Medicine and Allied Sciences*, *19* (1964), 389–417.

Debus, Allen G. "Sir Thomas Browne and the Study of Colour Indicators", *Ambix*, *10* (1962), 29–36.

Debus, Allen G. "Solution Analyses Prior to Robert Boyle", *Chymia*, *8* (1962), 41–61.

Debus, Allen G. "The Sun in the Universe of Robert Fludd", *Actes* of the Colloque international organisé par l'Institut pour l'Étude de la Renaissance et de l'Humanisme de l'Université de Bruxelles—"Le Soleil à la Renaissance—Sciences et Mythes" (in press).

Delaunay, P. *La Vie Médicale aux 16ième, 17ième Siècles*. Paris, 1935.

Duffy, P. H. "The Theory and Practice of Medicine in Elizabethan England." Unpublished Ph.D. dissertation, Harvard University, 1942.

Dufrenoy, M. L., and Dufrenoy, J. "The Significance of antimony in the history of chemistry", *Journal of Chemical Education*, *27* (1950), 595–97.

Edgar, Irving I. "Elizabethan conceptions of the physiology of the circulation", *Annals of Medical History*, *8* (1936), 359–70.

Evans, George H. "The Contribution of Francis Anthony to Medicine", *Annals of Medical History*, *2* (1940), 171–73.

Fleming, Donald. "Galen on the Motion of the Blood in the Heart and Lungs", *Isis, 46* (1955), 14–21.

Fletcher, Robert. "Medical lore in the older English dramatists and poets", *Bulletin of Johns Hopkins Hospital, 6* (Baltimore, 1895), 73–84.

Garrison, Fielding H. *An Introduction to the History of Medicine.* 4th ed. London, 1929.

Gentili, Giuseppe A. "Leonardo Fioravanti Bolognese alla luce di ignorati documenti", *Revista di storia delle scienze, 42* (1951), 16–41.

Gibson, Thomas. "A Sketch of the Career of Theodore Turquet de Mayerne", *Annals of Medical History*, New Series, *5* (1933), 315–26.

Giordano, D. *Leonardo Fioravanti Bolognese.* Bologna, 1920.

Gollan, Josué. *La Alquimia.* Santa Fe, Argentina, 1956.

Goodall, Charles (Dr.). *The Royal College of Physicians of London Founded and Established by Law; As appears by Letters, Patents, Acts of Parliament, adjudged Cases, etc., and An Historical Account of the College's proceedings against Empiricks and unlicensed Practisers in every Princes Reign from their first Incorporation to the Murther of the Royal Martyr, King Charles the First.* London, 1684.

Gottlieb, Bernward Joseph. "Elgans de septo cordis pervio observatio", *Sudhoffs Archiv für Geschichte der Medizin, 41* (1957), 345–48.

Graves, F. P. *Petrus Ramus and the Educational Reformation of the Sixteenth Century.* New York, 1912.

Guerlac, Henry. "John Mayow and the Aerial Nitre—Studies in the chemistry of John Mayow, I", *Actes de Septième Congrès International d'Histoire des Sciences* (Jerusalem, août, 1953), 332–49.

Guerlac, Henry. "The Poets' Nitre. Studies in the chemistry of John Mayow—II", *Isis, 45* (1954), 243–55.

Guitard, E. H. *Le Prestigieux Passé des Eaux minérales.* Paris, 1951.

Harris, L. E. *The Two Netherlanders. Humphrey Bradley and Cornelis Drebbel.* Leiden, 1961.

Hirsch, Rudolf. "The invention of printing and the diffusion of alchemical and chemical knowledge", *Chymia, 3* (1950), 115–41.

Hoefer, Ferdinand. *Histoire de la Chimie.* 2 vols. Paris, 1842–43.

Holmyard, E. J. *Alchemy.* Edinburgh, 1957.

Holmyard, E. J. *Makers of Chemistry.* Oxford, 1931.

Hooykaas, R. "Chemical Trichotomy before Paracelsus?", *Archives Internationales d'Histoire des Sciences, 28* (1949), 1063–74.

Hooykaas, R. "Die chemische Verbindung bei Paracelsus", *Archiv für Geschichte der Medizin, 32* (1939), 166–75.

Hooykaas, R. "Die Elementenlehre der iatrochemiker", *Janus, 41* (1937), 1–28.

Hooykaas, R. "Die Elementenlehre des Paracelsus", *Janus*, *39* (1935), 175–88.

Hooykaas, R. "The Experimental Origin of Chemical Atomic and Molecular Theory Before Boyle", *Chymia*, 2 (1949), 65–80.

Hopkins, A. P. *Alchemy, Child of Greek Philosophy*. New York, 1934.

Hort, G. M. *Dr. John Dee, Elizabethan mystic and astrologer*. London, 1922.

Hutin, Serge. *Robert Fludd, Le Rosicrucien*. Paris, 1953.

Isaacs, Raphael. "Medicine in the seventeenth century in England", in *Victor Robinson Memorial Volume*. New York, 1948.

Johnson, Francis R. *Astronomical Thought in Renaissance England*. Baltimore, 1937.

Johnson, Francis R. "Latin versus English: the sixteenth century debate over scientific terminology", *Studies in Philology*, 41 (1944), 109–35.

Johnson, Francis R. "A Newe Herball of Macer and Banckes's Herball: Notes on Robert Wyer and the Printing of Cheap Handbooks of Science in the Sixteenth Century", *Bulletin of the History of Medicine*, *15* (1944), 246–60.

Johnson, Francis R. "Thomas Hill: An Elizabethan Huxley", *Huntington Library Quarterly*, 7 (1944), 329–51.

Jones, R. F. *Ancients and Moderns*. St. Louis, 1936.

Josten, C. H. "Robert Fludd's 'Philosophicall Key' and his Alchemical Experiment on Wheat", *Ambix*, *11* (1963), 1–23.

Josten, C. H. "Truth's Golden Harrow. An unpublished alchemical treatise of Robert Fludd in the Bodleian Library", *Ambix*, *3* (1949), 91–150.

Jung, C. G. *Psychology and Alchemy*. Bollingen Series XX. New York, 1953.

King, Lester. *The Growth of Medical Thought*. Chicago, 1963.

Kirkby, William. *The Evolution of Artificial Mineral Waters*. Manchester, 1902.

Kocher, Paul H. "John Hester, Paracelsan (fl. 1576–93)", in *Joseph Quincy Adams Memorial Studies*, edited by James G. McManaway, Giles E. Dawson, Edwin E. Willoughby. Washington, 1948.

Kocher, Paul H. "Paracelsan Medicine in England (ca. 1570–1600)", *Journal of the History of Medicine*, 2 (1947), 451–80.

Kocher, Paul H. *Science and Religion in Elizabethan England*. San Marino, California, 1953.

Kopp, Hermann. *Geschichte der Chemie*. 4 vols. Braunschweig, 1843, 1844, 1845, 1847.

Kopp, Hermann. *Geschichte der Chemie*. 4 vols., published in 2. Leipzig, 1931.

Koyré, Alexander. *Mystiques, spirituels, alchimistes. Schwenckfeld, Seb. Franck, Weigel, Paracelse*. Paris, 1955.

Kremers, Edward, and Urdang, George. *History of Pharmacy*. Philadelphia, 1951.

Kuhn, Thomas S. *The Copernican Revolution*. Cambridge, Mass., 1957.

Langdon-Brown, Sir Walter, M.D. "John Caius and the Revival of Learning", *Proceedings of the Royal Society of Medicine, 35* (1941), 61–69.

Larkey, Sanford V. "The Hippocratic Oath in Elizabethan England", *Bulletin of the Institute of the History of Medicine, 4* (1936), 201–19.

Larkey, Sanford V. *Medical Knowledge in Tudor England as displayed in an Exhibition of Books and Manuscripts*. San Marino, California, 1935.

Larkey, Sanford V. "Scientific Glossaries in sixteenth century English books", *Bulletin of the Institute of the History of Medicine, 5* (1937), 105–14.

Larkey, Sanford V. "The Vesalian compendium of Geminus and Nicholas Udall's translation: their relation to Vesalius, Caius, Vicary and De Mondeville." Reprinted from the *Transactions of the Bibliographical Society*, March, 1933.

Larkey, Sanford V. and Temkin, Owsei. "John Banister and the pulmonary circulation", in *Essays in Biology in honor of Herbert M. Evans*. Berkeley, 1943.

Lasswitz, Kurd. *Geschichte der Atomistik vom Mittelalter bis Newton*. 2 vols. Hamburg, 1890.

Le Clerc, Daniel, M.D. *The History of Physick*. Translated by Dr. Drake and Dr. Baden. London, 1699.

Leggett, William F. *Ancient and Medieval Dyes*. Brooklyn, New York, 1944.

Lieb, Fritz. *Valentin Weigels Kommentar zur Schöpfungsgeschichte und das Schrifttum seines Schülers Benedikt Biedermann*. Zürich, 1962.

Lenoble, Robert. *Mersenne ou La Naissance du Mécanisme*. Paris, 1943.

Lindroth, Sten. *Paracelsismen i Sverige till 1600—talets mitt*. Uppsala, 1943.

Lloyd, O. M. "The Royal College of Physicians of London and some City Livery Companies", *Journal of the History of Medicine, 11* (1956), 412–21.

Major, Ralph H. "William Clowes (1544–1604) and his 'profitable and Necessarie Booke of Observations'", *Annals of Medical History, 4* (1932), 1–11.

Marcham, F. G. "Letters of an English Physician in the early XVIIth century", *Isis, 16* (1931), 55–81.

Martin-Charpenel, Georges. "Gassendi physiologiste", in *Actes du Congrès du Tricentenaire de Pierre Gassendi* (4–7 août, 1955). Digne, 1957.

Matthews, Leslie G. *History of Pharmacy in Britain.* Edinburgh and London, 1962.

Maynard, K. "Science in early English literature, 1550-1650", *Isis, 17* (1932), 94-126.

Mazzeo, Joseph A. "Notes on John Donne's Alchemical Imagery", *Isis, 48* (1957), 103-23.

Metzger, Hélène. "La philosophie chimique de Jean-Baptiste van Helmont", *Ann. Guébhard-Séverine, 12* (1936), 140-56.

Metzger, Hélène. *Les Doctrines chimiques en France du début du XVIIe à la fin du XVIIIe Siècle.* Première partie. Paris, 1923.

Milt, Bernhard. "Conrad Gesner als Balneologe", *Gesnerus, 2* (1945), 1-16.

Moore, Norman. *The History of the Study of Medicine in the British Isles.* Oxford, 1908.

More, L. T. *Life and Works of Robert Boyle.* London, 1944.

Mullett, Charles F. *The Bubonic Plague and England: an essay in the history of preventive medicine.* Lexington, Ky., 1956.

Mullett, Charles F. "Hugh Plat: Elizabethan virtuoso", *University of Missouri Studies, 21* (1947), 93-118.

Mullett, Charles F. "Public Baths and Health in England, Sixteenth–Eighteenth Century", *Supplement to the Bulletin of the History of Medicine*, No. 5, 1946.

Multhauf, Robert. "The Beginning of Mineralogical Chemistry", *Isis, 49* (1958), 50-53.

Multhauf, Robert. "John of Rupescissa and the Origin of Medical Chemistry", *Isis, 45* (1954), 359-67.

Multhauf, Robert. "Medical Chemistry and the Paracelsians", *Bulletin of the History of Medicine, 28* (1954), 101-26.

Multhauf, Robert. "The Significance of Distillation in Renaissance Medical Chemistry", *Bulletin of the History of Medicine, 30* (1956), 329-46.

Murray, W. A., "Donne and Paracelsus: An Essay in Interpretation", *The Review of English Studies, 25* (1949), 115-23.

Neuberger, Dr. Max. *Geschichte der Medizin.* Vol. 2. Stuttgart, 1911.

Neuberger, Max. "Some Relations between British and German medicine in the seventeenth century", in *Essays in the History of Medicine presented to Professor Arturo Castiglioni.* Baltimore, 1944.

Nordenskiold, Erik. *The History of Biology.* New York, 1946.

Pachter, Henry M. *Paracelsus, Magic Into Science.* New York, 1951.

Pagel, Walter. *Das Medizinische Weltbild des Paracelsus: seine Zusammen-hänge mit Neuplatonismus und Gnosis.* Wiesbaden, 1962.

Pagel, Walter. "Giordano Bruno: the Philosophy of Circles and the

Circular Movement of the blood", *Journal of the History of Medicine, 6* (1951), 116–24.

Pagel, Walter. *Paracelsus*. Basel, 1958.

Pagel, Walter. "Paracelsus and the Neoplatonic and Gnostic Tradition", *Ambix, 8* (1960), 125–66.

Pagel, Walter. "The Philosophy of Circles—Cesalpino—Harvey. A Penultimate Assessment", *Journal of the History of Medicine, 12* (1957), 140–57.

Pagel, Walter. "The Position of Harvey and van Helmont in the History of European Thought. To commemorate H. E. Sigerist's Essay on Harvey (1928)", *Journal of the History of Medicine, 13* (1958), 186–99.

Pagel, Walter. "The Prime Matter of Paracelsus", *Ambix, 9* (1961), 117–35.

Pagel, Walter. "The Religious and Philosophical aspects of van Helmont's science and medicine", *Supplement to the Bulletin of the History of Medicine, No. 2*. Baltimore, 1944.

Pagel, Walter. "Religious Motives in the Medical Biology of the XVIIth Century", *Bulletin of the Institute of the History of Medicine, 3* (1935), 97–128, 213–31, 265–312.

Pagel, Walter. "William Harvey and the Purpose of Circulation", *Isis, 42* (1951), 22–38.

Partington, J. R. *A History of Chemistry*. Vol. 2, London, 1961; Vol. 3, London, 1963.

Partington, J. R. "Joan Baptista van Helmont", *Annals of Science, 1* (1936), 359–84.

Partington, J. R. "The Life and Work of John Mayow (1641–1679)", *Isis, 47* (1956), 217-30, 405–17.

Partington, J. R. *Origins and Development of Applied Chemistry*. London, 1935.

Partington, J. R. "Paracelsus (1493–1541)", *Nature, 148* (1941), 332–34.

Partington, J. R. *A Short History of Chemistry*. London, 1951.

Pauli, W. "The Influence of Archetypal Ideas on the Scientific Theories of Kepler", in C. G. Jung and W. Pauli, *The Interpretation of Nature and the Psyche*. Translated by Priscilla Silz. New York, 1955.

Pazzini, Adalberti. "Paracelso e l'umanesimo italiano", *Istituto di storia della medicina della R. Universita di Roma*. Rome, 1941.

Peller, Sigismund. "Harvey's and Cesalpino's Role in the History of Medicine", *Bulletin of the History of Medicine, 23* (1949), 213–15.

Pfester, Hedwig. *Bad Kissinger vor Vierhundert Jahren*. Wurzburg, 1954.

Poole, H. Edmund. *The Wisdom of Andrew Boorde*. Leicester, 1936.

Power, Sir D'Arcy. "The Beginnings of the Literary Renaissance of Surgery in England", *Proceedings of the Royal Society of Medicine, 22* (1928), 77–82.

Power, D'Arcy. "Dr. Walter Bayley and his Works, 1529–1592", *Medico-Chirurgical Transactions*, 90 (London, 1907), 415–54.

Power, Sir D'Arcy. "Epoch Making Books in British Surgery. V. The Surgeons Mate by John Woodall", *British Journal of Surgery*, 16 (1928), 1–5.

Power, Sir D'Arcy. *Medicine in the British Isles*. New York, 1930.

Poynter, F. N. L., and Bishop, W. J. "A Seventeenth-Century Doctor and his Patients: John Symcotts, 1592(?)–1662", publication of the *Bedfordshire Historical Record Society*, No. 31 (1951). Streatley, near Luton, Beds.

Poynter, F. N. L. "A Seventeenth-Century Medical Controversy: Robert Witty versus William Simpson", *Science, Medicine and History*, 2 (1953), 72–81.

Price, George R. "Medical Men in A Faire Quarrell", *Bulletin of the History of Medicine*, 24 (1950), 38–42.

Radbill, Samuel X. "John Jones, phisition, The second writer on pediatrics in English", *Bulletin of the Institute of the History of Medicine*, 6 (1938), 145–62.

Rath, Gernat. "Die Anfänge der Mineral Quellenanalyse", *Medizinischen Monatsschrift*, 3 (1949), 539–41.

Rath, Gernat. "Die Mineralquellenanalyse im 17. Jahrhundert", *Sudhoffs Archiv für Geschichte der Medizin und der Naturwissenschaften*, 41 (1957), 1–9.

Raven, Charles E., D.D. *English Naturalists from Neckam to Ray*. Cambridge, 1947.

Read, John. *Prelude to Chemistry*. New York, 1937.

Robbins, Frank Egleston. *The Hexaemeral Literature*. Chicago, 1912.

Robertson, W. H. Aitchison. "The Castel of Helth and its author, Sir Thomas Elyot", *Annals of Medical History*, 1 (1929), 270–83.

Santillana, Giorgio de. *The Age of Adventure: The Renaissance Philosophers*. New York, 1956.

Santillana, Giorgio de. "The Seventeenth-Century Legacy: Our Mirror of Being", in *Science and the Modern Mind, A Symposium*. Edited by Gerald Holton. Boston, 1948.

Sarton, George. *Appreciation of Ancient and Medieval Science During the Renaissance*. New York, 1961.

Sarton, George. *Introduction to the History of Science*. 3 vols. in 5 parts. Baltimore, 1927–48.

Sarton, George. *Six Wings: Men of Science in the Renaissance*. Bloomington, Indiana, 1957.

Schneider, Wolfgang. "A Bibliographical Review of the History of

Pharmaceutical Chemistry", *American Journal of Pharmaceutical Education*, 23 (1959), 161–72.

Schneider, Wolfgang. "Die deutschen Pharmakopöen des 16. Jahrhunderts und Paracelsus", *Pharmazeutische Zeitung*, 106 (1961), 3–15.

Schneider, Wolfgang. "Probleme und neuere Ansichten in der Alchemiegeschichte", *Chemiker-Zeitung—Chem. Apparatur*, 85 (1961), 643–52.

Schneider, Wolfgang. "Der Wandel des Arzneischatzes im 17. Jahrhundert und Paracelsus", *Sudhoffs Archiv für Geschichte der Medizin und der Naturwissenschaften*, 45 (1961), 201–15.

Sherlock, T. P. "The Chemical Work of Paracelsus", *Ambix*, 3 (1948), 33–63.

Shirley, John W. "The Scientific Experiments of Sir Walter Raleigh, the Wizard Earl, and the Three Magi in the Tower, 1603-1617", *Ambix*, 4 (1949), 52–66.

Sigerist, Henry E. *A Fifteenth Century Surgeon: Hieronymus Brunschwig and His Work.* New York, 1946.

Singer, Charles. *The Discovery of the Circulation of the Blood.* London, 1922.

Singer, Charles. *The Earliest Chemical Industry.* London, 1948.

Singer, Charles Joseph. *Early English Magic and Medicine.* London, 1920.

Singer, Charles. *Short History of Medicine.* New York, 1928.

Singer, Charles. *A Short History of Scientific Ideas to 1900.* Oxford, 1959.

Stearns, Raymond Phineas. "The Scientific Spirit in England in Early Modern Times (c. 1600)", *Isis*, 34 (1943), 293–99.

Stillman, John Maxson. "Chemistry in medicine in the fifteenth century", *Science Monthly*, 6 (1918), 167–75.

Stillman, John Maxson. *Paracelsus.* Chicago, 1920.

Sudhoff, Karl. "The Literary Remains of Paracelsus", in *Essays in the History of Medicine.* New York, 1926.

Tallmadge, G. Kasten. "Caecilius Folius on the Circulation", *Bulletin of the History of Medicine*, 28 (1954), 15–31.

Taylor, Frank Sherwood. *The Alchemists, Founders of Modern Chemistry.* New York, 1949.

Telepnef, Basilio de. *Paracelsus, A Genius Amidst a Troubled World.* St. Gall, 1945.

Thomas, Sir Henry. "The Society of Chymical Physitians, an echo of the Great Plague of London", *Science, Medicine and History*, 2 (1953), 56–71.

Thompson, C. J. S. *The Quacks of Old London.* New York, 1928.

Thorndike, L. *A History of Magic and Experimental Science.* 8 vols. New York, 1923–58.

Tierie, Gerrit. *Cornelis Drebbel (1572-1633).* Amsterdam, 1932.

Underwood, F. Ashworth. "Pharmacy and Therapeutics in the Age of Elizabeth I", *Pharmaceutical Journal, 170* (1953), 406–07, 411–15.

Urdang, George. "How Chemicals Entered the Official Pharmacopoeias", *Archives Internationales d'Histoire des Sciences, 7* (1954), 303–14.

Urdang, George. "The Mystery About the First English (London) Pharmacopoeia (1618)", *Bulletin of the History of Medicine, 12* (1942), 304–13.

Waite, Arthur Edward. *The Real History of the Rosicrucians.* London, 1887.

Waite, Arthur Edward. *The Secret Tradition in Alchemy.* London, 1926.

Webb, Henry J. "English Military Surgery During the Age of Elizabeth", *Bulletin of the History of Medicine, 15* (1944), 261–75.

Weil, E. "The Echo of Harvey's De Motu Cordis (1628) 1628 to 1657", *Journal of the History of Medicine, 12* (1957), 167–74.

Westfall, Richard S. *Science and Religion in Seventeenth-Century England.* New Haven, 1958.

Wright, Louis B. *Middle Class Culture in Elizabethan England.* Chapel, N.C., 1935.

Young, Sidney. *Annals of the Barber Surgeons of London.* London, 1890.

3. DICTIONARIES, AND BIOGRAPHICAL AND BIBLIOGRAPHICAL AIDS

Boissard, Ian. Iacobus. *Bibliotheca sive Thesaurus Virtutis et Gloriae: In quo continentur Illustrium Eruditione & doctrina Virorum Effigies & Vitae.* 5 parts. Frankfurt, 1628–32.

Bolton, Henry Carrington. *Select Bibliography of Chemistry, 1482–1892.* Washington, 1893, Supp. 1, 1899, Supp. 2, 1904.

Castelli, Bartholomaeus. *Lexicon Medicum.* Padua, 1721.

Dictionary of National Biography. 22 vols. London, 1949–50.

Duveen, Denis I. *Bibliotheca alchemica et chemica.* London, 1949.

Ferguson, John. *Bibliotheca chemica. A catalogue of the alchemical, chemical, and pharmaceutical books in the collection of the late James Young.* 2 vols. Glasgow, 1906.

Ferguson, John. "Some English Alchemical Books", *The Journal of the Alchemical Society, 2* (1913), 2–16.

Fuller, Thomas. *The Worthies of England.* Edited by John Freeman. London, 1952.

Garrison, Fielding H., and Morton, Leslie T. *A Medical Bibliography: A Check-list of Texts Illustrating the History of the Medical Sciences.* London, 1943.

Gesner, Conrad. *Bibliotheca Universalis*. Tiguri, 1545.

Lavoisier, Fourcroy, Morveau, Cadet, Baume, d'Arcet, et Sage. *Nomenclature Chimique*. Nouvelle édition. Paris, 1789.

Maunsell, Andrew. *The Seconde parte of the Catalogue of English printed Bookes*. (Scientific books.) London, 1595.

De Morveau, Lavoisier, Bertholet, and De Fourcroy. *Method of Chymical Nomenclature*. Translated by James St. John, M.D. London, 1788.

Munk, William. *The Roll of the Royal College of Physicians of London: comprising biographical sketches*. 2nd ed. 3 vols. London, 1878.

Pernety, Antoine-Joseph. *Dictionnaire Mytho-Hermétique*. Paris, 1787.

Pollard, A. W., and Redgrave, G. R. *A Short Title Catalogue of Books Printed in England, Scotland, and Ireland . . . 1475–1640*. London, 1926.

Ruland, Martin. *Lexicon Alchemiae sive Dictionarium Alchemisticum*. Frankfurt, 1612.

Russell, K. F. "Check List of Medical Books Published in English Before 1600", *Bulletin of the History of Medicine*, 21 (1947), 922–58.

Sudhoff, Karl. "Ein Beitrag zur Bibliographie der Paracelsisten in 16. Jahrhundert", *Centralblatt für Bibliothekswesen*, 10 (1893), 316–26, 385–407.

Sudhoff, Karl. *Versuch einer Kritik der Echtheit der Paracelsischen Schriften*. 2 vols. Berlin, 1894, 1899.

Index